IN

THE

BEGINNING

by
Roger D. G. Price

NEW WINE PRESS

© 1979 Roger Price
Revised edition 1991

New Wine Press
P.O. Box 17
Chichester
West Sussex PO20 6YB
England

ISBN 0 947852 83 2

Printed in Great Britain by Richard Clay Ltd, Bungay, Suffolk.

To the members of the Chichester Christian Fellowship whose encouragement and support over many years has been a source of inspiration and comfort. Without them this book would never have been written.

Contents

Foreword

It was about three years ago that I started persuading Roger Price to begin writing up his lectures, talks and thoughts, thus making them available to the public at large. It is a pleasure to see that he has made a good start and I am hoping that this book will be followed by many others. I consider him an eminent scholar in a general sense, with a particularly outstanding knowledge of biblical times and the Bible itself, as well as a born teacher with the rare ability of conveying complex matters in a simple form which makes them easy to grasp.

In this book he presents data and information, including many of the latest findings in various spheres of science; these results of scholarly research show the validity of the Genesis account of Creation and the folly of the theory of evolution.

As an aftermath of nineteenth-century scientific thinking there still are many in our times who proclaim the theory of evolution as fact, ignoring the turn in reasoning that scientists themselves took earlier this century, probably starting with Einstein. The application of his theories, for example, initiated a change of thinking in relation to the formation of this planet, the history of mankind and the shaping of life into what we see it as today. This change in approach has not taken us further away from the Biblical truth, but has brought us much nearer to it in the sense that the more scientists have discovered, the further away the horizons of knowledge have receded and the more we have had to admit to our own limitations. Beyond what can be proved, the possibility remains open for each of us to find the answers in God and in His creative powers or in some theory; science cannot prove or disprove the greatest of mysteries.

Our generation has a keen interest in digging for deeper truths. Once liberated from the assumption that science has excluded the validity of Biblical teaching, many have found immense growth in their understanding of God and His word. Although faith can neither be originated nor made to grow by argument — sound argument can open the way for honest seekers.

This is precisely what Roger Price's book does: by liberating minds it removes some obsructive stones from the way of the 'diggers'.

George Ray
Visiting Professor of Economics,
University of Surrey, Guildford.

Preface

This book has been written to satisfy a need felt by many people for a clear yet concise analysis of the view Bible-believing Christians take about the Creation of the earth and its subsequent development. While there are a great number of books already published about the Biblical view of creation I have felt them either to be aimed at a specialized readership or to be rather too simplistic.

The aim of this book is to provide a sufficiently detailed coverage of the subject and to bring together the various scientific disciplines into a united overall pattern with appeal to Christian and non-Christian, academic and layman, teacher and student alike.

While the time to write the book came only because of the cancellation of a conference earlier this year, it has nevertheless been developing in my thoughts for some years. When I became a Christian I soon saw for the first time how many of my views had been based on things which while presented as fact were actually theory, and while attempting a reassessment found my path littered with my own untested assumptions. I soon became dismayed at the unquestioning acceptance and dogmatism surrounding the Theory of Evolution in schools and colleges, and the intolerance shown towards any gainsaying it.

Worse than that was the unwillingness of most Christians to support and defend the account of creation given in the first three chapters of the Bible. They were afraid to view Genesis scientifically and often too, unwilling to labour to justify the claims of Scripture.

My prayer is that the book will be a source of inspiration to many and that, having the courage of their convictions, in true loyalty to the Lord they will be ready always to give an answer to every man who asks them.

I commit this book into His hands that He may use it as He desires. Fortunately for us 'it is with Him that we have to do'.

Roger D. G. Price
April 1979

Preface to the Revised Edition

In the past 12 years interest in 'creationism' around the world has increased enormously, especially in Eastern Europe, Russia, Korea, and not least in Great Britain. A large number of books have been published, by Christians and non-Christians exposing the fallacies of Evolution. However, members of the Chichester Christian Fellowship feel that Roger Price's contribution is still an excellent introduction for the non-specialist reader, demonstrating that the facts of science do not contradict the clear statements of Scripture regarding Origins, and do support the historical records of a global Flood.

David C. C. Watson M.A.(Cantab.)
April 1991

Acknowledgements

The writer wishes to express his thanks to Malcolm Coulson who has spent so many hours painstakingly correcting the proofs. His ceaseless care, enthusiasm and helpful comments have enhanced the manuscript greatly.

All the delightful illustrations in this book are the inspired work of Jenny New (now Mrs Jenny Davis), and to her must go much of the credit for the attractiveness of the volume.

Typing of proofs is an arduous task and Jill Sayers must receive credit for being uncomplaining and prompt.

Ed Harding has given excellent advice about the production and design of the book.

Last, but not least, I must thank my wife for her love and encouragement. Her broad scope of knowledge has been invaluable.

All errors are entirely my own.

CHAPTER ONE

The Alternatives

Man has always been an explorer. His insatiable desire for answers to the questions How? When? Why? and Where? has been evidenced by a history of exploration, navigation and scientific investigation. This is the reason why man has been found in the most extreme environments: in waterless deserts, hot and humid jungles, bleak icy wastes and more recently in the vacuum of space and at the pressurized ocean bottom. He has channelled his ingenuity and technological skill into making instruments to assist his search—telescopes to widen his horizons, microscopes to deepen his probings and every type of mechanical device to extend the frontiers of human understanding. Yet however much man explores and seeks knowledge, he will always be confronted by certain unknowns and limitations. He can neither foresee the future nor be an eyewitness to the events of the distant past, hence the future is a total blank and the past a hazy blur.

The Bible declares that 'the fear of the Lord is the beginning of wisdom' Psalm 111 : 10, yet ever since the Fall, man has striven to be free and independent of God, even to the extent of rejecting solutions which involve God. It is currently fashionable to consider that any solution involving God's action is a naive solution. This result is best expressed in the words of G. K. Chesterton who said "When men cease to believe in God, they do not believe in nothing but in anything." This is why many of the so-called scientific solutions to origins are actually non-scientific and in some cases contradict the known laws of science and why facts which threaten cherished theories have been discarded or simply ignored.

1

Two examples will serve to demonstrate the point. It is a well established law that if a rotating body breaks up then the pieces which fly off will spin in the same direction as the original body.

Similarly, particles formed from a swirling mass of condensing gas will have the same direction of rotation as the original mass. Mathematicians call this the conservation of angular momentum.

Some scientists believe that the Sun and its satellites resulted from the condensation of such a mass of gas. If this is true then all the planets and their moons should revolve around the sun, and rotate about their axes in the same direction. Yet in the Solar System this is not the case. Venus rotates in the opposite direction to the other planets and backwards in relation to its movement round the Sun; Uranus rotates on its side at 98° to its orbital movement around the Sun, and twenty one of the

3

fifty two moons of the Solar System—over one third—go round their planets in a retrograde direction. Yet Dr. Isaac Asimov in his book 'The Intelligent Man's Guide to Science'[1] says that these retrograde satellites are 'minor exceptions'!

A second example involves the Second Law of Thermo-dynamics which states that in a closed system the proportion of energy available to perform work diminishes. A man winding a watch is putting energy into the watch but as he is winding it some energy is made into heat by overcoming friction. Hence the energy the watch has to move the arms is less than the amount of energy he put in.

The law can be expressed in another way—that there is a tendency towards randomness within the Universe. This means that less complex distributions of matter form from more complex ones or simply that order proceeds to chaos. Things which begin in an orderly state will become less and less orderly with time and things which begin in a chaotic state cannot become ordered, but become more and more chaotic. Yet the proposed Theory of Evolution is said to be the one thing that contradicts this law. Evolutionists believe that an initial chaotic state of matter developed into a complex ordered state i.e. chaos proceeded to order. So it is that Lord Porter in his book 'The Laws of Disorder' states "whereas all observed phenomena demonstrate the second law of thermo-dynamics, there is another trend which seems diametrically opposed to this; the creation and evolution of life." He then dismisses this exception with the statement, "we need not be concerned about our precious second law" going on to explain that the energy from the sun "is already available to provide the driving force which enables the part of the Universe called life to increase its order." With such statements the evolutionist convinces himself that the Theory of Evolution and the second law of thermodynamics are not contradictory.

While it is true that the sun's energy is available, he fails to suggest the mechanism by which allegedly this energy was converted and directed to produce life and the subsequent increase in order. "Chance" Porter says, "dealt a winning hand, a most improbable arrangement perhaps, but one which had the power to reproduce its kind." [2]

The fallacy of this 'improbable arrangement' is obvious. Men building houses or birds building nests accomplish the task with an input of energy, but energy alone is not enough. Intelligence and skill are needed to direct the energy meaningfully. Chance is no replacement for design.

Robin

Excluding God's action and design means that all that is seen around us today must be the result of factors currently observable, working continuously and for long periods of time in the past. The arrangement of Planets in the Solar System and their movements must be explained in terms of the interaction of heavenly bodies upon one another. So cosmogenists and others theorize about the origin of the Solar System on the assumption that the laws of planetary motion and applied mathematics alone must be responsible for what has happened.

This attitude is not limited to the academic world. Scientists and schoolboys alike have been inculcated with it. The whole question of whether or not there is life on other planets, for example, is considered in an entirely evolutionary way. The answer given by Patrick Moore and by the majority of people today follows the line of reasoning that the Universe is so vast that there is a chance that somewhere among the millions and millions of bodies in space there is one which has just the right conditions for life to have begun and to be sustained. Evolutionists therefore claim that life will begin given the right conditions—a combination of the right chemicals, radiation and chance reactions dictate life's existence, not the intervention of a Supreme Creator.

This is why millions of pounds have been spent trying to contact other civilizations in space, and why intricate mini-laboratories have been sent to Mars to see whether life has existed there. Two evolutionists, Miller & Urey, express it well: 'Surely one of the most marvellous feats of 20th Century science would be the firm proof that life exists on another planet. All the projected space flights and the high costs of such developments would be fully justified if they were able to establish the existence of life on either Mars or Venus. In that case, the thesis that life develops spontaneously when the conditions are favourable would be far more firmly established and our whole view of the problem of the origin of life would be confirmed.'[3]

Unfortunately for them, the experiments carried out on the surface of Mars have led many to the unavoidable conclusion that life does not exist and never has existed on that planet. The evolutionists, however, remain undismayed and continue in their quest to explain every observable fact within an evolutionary framework—if it exists, they say, it must have evolved.

Man, the evolutionists say, walks upright and breathes with lungs not by design but because of a series of environmental pressures and chance happenings which caused him to develop lungs and made him abandon his former posture of being 'on all fours'. The details of this development and those in many other cases are unknown and not proved, but as it is certainly assumed that God didn't create, there is no alternative.

There are many people today who believe that life has already been created by scientists in the laboratory. They also believe that the generation of cells given the right conditions is a proven fact.

Actually the synthesis from inorganic matter to a cell capable of reproducing itself is far more complex than most laymen think. There are several distinct steps in such a process:-

1. The formation of the basic amino acids from inorganic compounds.

2. The formation of peptide bonds and proteins—complex arrangements of the amino acids.

3. The formation of cells.

It is not just one step to life but at least three, and while it is certainly true that the first step has been achieved, the other steps get progressively larger and more unattainable. It is interesting to note that even with the first relatively simple step, problems have arisen which make progression to the following step extremely unlikely.

The most famous experiment in the formation of amino acids is that of Stanley L. Miller. This experiment was based on the assumption that the atmosphere of the primitive earth was not like the atmosphere today but instead consisted of hydrogen, methane, ammonia and water vapour. There is no proof that the atmosphere of the earth was like that, but as they admit, this atmosphere is 'favourable for the production of organic compounds which make up life as we know it.'[4] In other words, these are the chemicals which they know will produce the amino acids!

Having collected this atmosphere it was then necessary to expose it to free energy in the form of ultra-violet radiation and electric discharges, the former of which would affect the earth in an oxygen- or ozone-free atmosphere, and the latter of which would represent primitive thunderstorms. When this was done he found that a number of amino acids including Glycine had been produced.

The arrangement of the apparatus used in this experiment is important. The primitive atmosphere was contained in a large glass container, while water vapour came from a smaller connected chamber and the resultant amino acids were collected in another much cooler container. The reason that the amino acids have to be removed from the atmospheric container is that if they are exposed to ultra-violet radiation for any length of time they are destroyed. In the laboratory such a removal is possible, but on the primitive earth it would have been impossible, so that if this process did occur, most of the resulting amino acids would have been destroyed.

If protection from ultra-violet radiation had come from the presence of an ozone layer as it does today, this would have meant the existence of oxygen in the atmosphere, and if oxygen had existed, then the amino acids would have been destroyed by oxidation. Either way so little of the amino acids would have remained in solution in the oceans, that the second step would have been impossible, as even the formation of more simple dipeptide links would require a very concentrated solution indeed.

The clear message from the Miller experiment is therefore that while amino acids do form under such conditions, this process could not have been the beginning of life on earth.

It is also important to see that proteins are not just linked pairs of amino acids but highly organized chains of amino acids, which increases the problem greatly. Duane T. Gish has estimated[5] that the probability of such complex order being formed by change is 1 in 10^{65} or 100 000 000 000 000 000 000 000 000 000 000 000 000 000 000 000 000 to 1. Such magnitude is beyond our comprehension.

Add to this the fact that the simplest cell contains thousands of kinds of proteins as well as DNA (DEOXYRIBONUCLEIC ACID) and RNA (RIBONUCLEIC ACID) and many other complex substances all arranged in an amazingly complex pattern then the true improbability of the evolution of a cell from inorganic compounds by chance can be seen.

Closer scrutiny reveals further problems. To make DNA, for example, protein is required; but the information necessary to make protein is contained in the DNA. So which came first? One cannot exist without the other. Surely then the production of a living cell can only be carried out by a similar living cell.

Despite these difficulties the search for the mechanisms necessary for life goes on because of the need to provide an explanation other than Divine intervention.

How definitely the Bible stands out against this view! The first verse of the Bible introduces One Who was before the Creation and Who is therefore Himself outside the Created realm and not subject to the laws of the Creation. 'In the beginning **God** created the heavens and the earth' Genesis 1: 1. He is the One who is the Designer and Planner of all that is seen around us. Here immediately is another alternative—that things in the Universe have been sovereignly planned and placed where they are; that all are His work. The Psalmist accepted this when he gazed at the night sky and said 'When I consider your heavens, the work of your fingers, the moon and the stars, which you have set in place,' Psalm 8: 3; God also revealed it when He asked Job "Where were you when I laid the earth's foundation?" Job 38: 4.

This too is the view of the early Church: not only did Paul state his belief in a Creator as in Colossians 1: 16—'for by Him all things were created'—but when arguing with the intellectuals of Athens he **began** his argument with the fact of a Creator—'God who made the world and everything in it'— Acts 17: 24.

Christians as a whole have been loath to face the obvious disagreement between Scripture and modern scientific thinking, most taking one of the simple but unsatisfactory solutions to the problem. Some take Genesis 1 to 11 as picture language employed to express complex truths, but even it if can be taken as picture language, it is clear that Jesus and the early Church took no such view. Remarkably, Genesis 1—11 is one of the most quoted sections of the Old Testament and every writer in the New Testament quotes from some part of it and quotes it as literal truth.

Jesus Himself quotes directly from Genesis 1, 2, 3, 4, 6 and 7.

Samples of Jesus' Quotations

Genesis 1   Matthew 19: 4 'Haven't you read . . . that at the beginning the Creator made them male and female.'

Genesis 2   Matthew 19: 5 'And said "For this reason a man will leave his father and mother and be united to his wife and the two shall become one flesh."'

Genesis 3   John 8: 44 'You belong to your father, the devil, and you want to carry out your father's desire. He was a murderer from the beginning, not holding to the truth, for there is no truth in him. When he lies, he speaks his native language, for he is a liar and the father of lies.'

10

Genesis 4   Luke 11: 51 'from the blood of Abel . . .'
Genesis 6 & 7 Luke 17: 26 and 27 'Just as it was in the days of Noah, so also will it be in the days of the Son of Man. People were eating and drinking, and marrying and being given in marriage up to the day Noah entered the ark. Then the flood came and destroyed them all.'

Genesis 8, 10 and 11 are quoted by Luke; Genesis 9 by the writer of the Book of Hebrews; and Paul quotes Genesis 1, 2, 3, & 4, using these passages as the base for much of his revelation about Christ and the Church.

To reject the literal nature of Genesis 1—11 is therefore to reject much of Jesus' own testimony and Paul's revelation. If **they** were wrong or naive over these issues, how do we know that they weren't wrong or naive over eternal things? Such a view can only lead to the rejection of the Word of God as a whole and once this is seen and faced up to by Christians, then the issues concerned in Genesis come clearly into focus. Jesus and all[6] of the Early Church believed in God's Creative act which lasted for a literal six days' duration and which occurred thousands, not millions, of years ago. They also believed in a literal Adam and Eve, in a literal Noah and in a literal Flood. No compromises can solve the Christian's dilemma—Jesus' Word is either true or false. If the Theory of Evolution is correct then it must reduce the Bible to the level of interesting myth and no more. This is the logical conclusion.

It is of note that Evolutionists no longer treat Evolution as a theory but uphold it as proven fact. Yet, as we shall see, evolution is very far from proven. What is more interesting is that very often Evolution, the Universe, Chance or 'Nature' are given religious status by evolutionists. To Bible-believing Creationists God has certain characteristics—He is:-

Sovereign
Omnipotent
Omnipresent
Omniscient
Eternal

God's Creation is none of these but is finite and within strict bounds.

To the Evolutionist, however, the Universe takes on those characteristics:

Sovereignty — Evolution decides and dictates the course of development.
Omnipotence — the huge changes necessary are effected by the forces of nature.
Omnipresence — The Universe has no boundaries but extends forever.
Omniscience — Science will eventually have all the answers to man's problems.
Eternity — Matter always will exist.

Many have been forced to the conclusion that Evolution is no more than an idolatrous religious system. If science is as the Oxford Dictionary states 'A branch of study which is concerned either with a connected body of demonstrated truths or with observed facts systematically classified and more or less colligated by being brought under general laws, and which includes trustworthy methods for the discovery of new truth within its own domain' then it involves **observed facts** and **demonstrated laws.** Therefore we must ask ourselves whether present evolutionary thought can be defined as science or not. If it is science, the observable facts must support it.

Before we consider these facts, however, let us examine the difference between Creation and Evolution.

CREATION

Creation begins with God. He created matter and ordered it in six days. In this system amino acids, proteins and cells came into existence together in an interdependent relationship by the creative act of God.

God	
Heaven and Earth* Water Light (not sunlight)	Day 1
Atmosphere	Day 2
Dry Land Land Vegetation	Day 3
Sun, Moon and Stars	Day 4
Sea Creatures Birds	Day 5
Land Creatures, Reptiles and Insects Man	Day 6

This was followed by a major catastrophe which occurred some thousands of years B.C. and during which rain fell for the first time on the earth.

EVOLUTION

The Evolutionist claims that matter came from nothing and that chance alone orders the progression to our current state.

Nothing	
Matter	
Stars and galaxies	
The sun and its planets including the Earth	
Atmosphere and water	
Simple cells	
Multi-cellular organisms	1,000's of millions of years.
Invertebrates	
Vertebrates including fish	
Amphibians	
Reptiles	
Birds	
Mammals	
Man	

The creation account and evolutionary theory are therefore widely divergent. No scheme can bridge this gap as the differences are too great.

In the next chapters we will examine some of the available data and see which of the two schemes they fit best.

* It must be said that for some years the author upheld the 'Gap Theory'; the theory that a gap of indeterminable length existed between Genesis 1 : 1 and 1 : 2 and that a whole former creation had existed and developed and had then been destroyed by a massive Flood. The six days' account being a later recreation on the Earth.

It was only recently that the author realized that such a theory is really 'a sop' to the evolutionists, and that the Gap Theory had very few answers to the real questions:- Did an evolutionary development occur before the Gap? Why were there remains of man before the Gap and were these men animals or did they have an eternal soul? If death came in because of Adam's sin, how and why was death manifest before the Gap? Why in Exodus 20 : 11 is it so clearly stated that the earth and heavens and **all** that is in them were created in six days? Did the sun and moon exist before the Gap? And so on.

The Gap Theory therefore produced a compromise solution which actually created more problems than it solved. The author is now convinced that Genesis 1 : 1 and the verses following explain a continuous process.

For a fuller discussion of this see: "What About Origins?" by Dr. A. J. Monty White, (Dunestone Printers, 1978) "The Early Earth", J. C. Whitcomb (Revised Edition, 1986, Baker Book House) and "Unformed and Unfilled", Weston Fields (Presbyterian and Reformed, 1976).

References
1. Dr. Isaac Asimov *'The Intelligent Man's Guide to Science'*. Vol. 1. p.78. 1950.
2. Sir George Porter *'The Laws of Disorder'*. B.B.C. Publications, 1965 pp.22-23.
3. Stanley L. Miller & Harold C. Urey *'Organic Compound Synthesis on the Primitive Earth'*. Science 31st July 1959. Vol. 130 p.251.
4. Ibid p.245.
5. Duane T. Gish *'Have you been....Brainwashed?'*. Life Messengers booklet. Box 1967, Seattle, Wa. 98111.
6. Origen and Augustine had problems with the Six Days of creation but they both emphatically believed in an Earth only a few thousand years old, and that Noah's Flood was universal. (Origen 'Against Celsus' I.19; IV.41; Augustine 'City of God' XV.27; XII.10).

CHAPTER TWO

How Old?

The evolutionist satisfies himself that anything can happen given sufficient time and so believes that by chance, chemical compounds interacting over long periods of time produced molecules and cells, and that living creatures adapting themselves over long periods of time developed new organs and limbs.

Thomas Huxley, an ardent evolutionist and supporter of Darwin, was reported to have said that if one million monkeys were typing on a million typewriters for one million years, then one of them by chance was bound to have typed a whole Shakespearean play. Here again vast numbers can lull most people into an acceptance of this statement but fortunately it is open to mathematical examination.

Let us make it much simpler and say that all we want the monkeys to type by chance is Genesis 1 : 1—"In the beginning God created the heavens and the earth" in capital letters. For this we need 26 capital letters and the spacing key on the typewriter—a total of only 27 keys. How long would it be before one of the million monkeys typed that sentence assuming they typed at 12 letters a second day in and day out?

The amount of time is so astronomical that we need a picture to describe it. Imagine a mountain so large that it filled the whole solar system with its base on the Earth and its top at the nearest star which is four light years away i.e. (4 x 186000 x 60 x 60 x 24 x 365 or 23,452,784,000,000 miles high). Imagine then that a bird comes **once** every 1000 years and removes the smallest grain of dust possible (0.0025″).

Four such mountains would have been removed before one of the monkeys had typed Genesis 1: 1!! In other words *far more time than we could ever allow*[1] *for evolution to have occurred.*

Now the evolutionist says that the earth is 4,600 million years old, which is a very small fraction of the time required by the monkeys to type Genesis 1 verse 1: indeed the typists would have hardly started warming up!! Compare this with the even greater period of time which would be required for the coming together of the amazingly complex structure of a living cell. Nevertheless evolutionists cling to their theories concerning origins.

We must now examine the basis for the evolutionist's belief that the earth is 4,600 million years old. According to the Bible, of course, it cannot be! As has already been said, some Bible believers have tried to avoid the issue of a literal six day creation by stating that each 'day' in Genesis One was not a literal day but a long period of time. They quote as proof the text in 2 Peter 3: 8 'one day is as a 1000 years'. This argument creates more problems than it solves for allowing a thousand years or even many thousands of years for each creation day would be insufficient to match the evolutionary age of 4,600 million years. It would require millions of years for each day.

The fact remains that Genesis One doesn't just say that these periods were days, it also says that each day was an evening and a morning. To compromise with the evolutionist therefore would require each day to be interpreted as millions of years of daylight followed by millions of years of night during which time any life forms which existed would perish.

Furthermore, if every day did represent a period of geological time the sequence of Creation given in the Bible still cannot be brought in line with the sequence the Evolutionists teach. A few examples will demonstrate this clearly:- Evolutionists say that the sun came into being before life on earth, the Bible says that vegetation was growing on the earth before the sun was made; evolutionists say that birds evolved from amphibians and reptiles, the Bible says that sea creatures and birds were made on the same day—and so on.

So what is it then that the Evolutionist uses to prove his stated age of the Earth?

There are several methods, but, unfortunately, all of them require definite assumptions which are neither proved nor provable. The basic absolute methods involve what is called RADIOMETRIC DATING.

This type of dating is based on the fact that some elements 'decay' over large periods of time to form other 'daughter' elements. For example uranium and thorium decay to form isotopes of lead; radioactive potassium decays to argon, rubidium to strontium and so on.

Therefore when a rock is found to contain uranium and lead, or potassium and argon, it is said that these can be used to assess the age of the rock simply because the period of decay can be calculated.

But this is where the assumptions begin. Let us take the potassium-argon system. They assume:

1. That there was **no** argon in the rock when it formed.

2. That all the argon found in the rock has come from decaying potassium.

3. That no argon formed from the potassium has been lost from the rock.

4. That no potassium has been lost from the rock.

5. That the rate of decay from potassium to argon has been constant.

None of these is provable, and some are extremely unlikely. How does one prove that all the argon in the rock came from potassium decay?—our atmosphere has a content of argon which could easily have been incorporated in the original rock, and all of which may not have come from decayed potassium.

In addition to these dubious assumptions, radiometric dating is fraught with the problem of practical inaccuracies. Dr. Earl Hallonquist, a Canadian chemist demonstrated this when he tested pieces of volcanic lava in Hawaii known to have formed in the years 1800 and 1801 and therefore to be less than 200 years old. He found that dating this lava by the Potassium-Argon tests produced a result of 160 million years.

The problem of Radiometric dating may be simply illustrated by this example. A man entering a room to find a 2 inch candle burning may wonder how long the candle has been alight. In order to calculate this he needs to know the following.

(a) How long the candle was when it was first made to burn.

(b) At what rate the candle burns.

(c) Whether the rate at which the candle burns is constant.

(d) Whether the candle has been continuously alight.

In considering radioactive decay in rocks there are corresponding unknowns, and unfortunately these remain unknowns. We do not know that there was no argon or lead in any given rock when it was formed. We do not know whether some potassium or thorium has been leached or washed out of the rock. We do not know that the rate of decay has been constant or continuous. This large number of unknowns has led to large assumptions as a basis for radiometric dating and hence to the unreliability of this method of dating.

Even if radiometric dating were accurate, the creationist's view of origins is that of an earth newly created yet appearing old. After all, when Adam was created, he was created as an adult. A doctor examining him one day after his creation would probably say "He's 30 years old", but he would actually only be a day old. Similarly, the wine made by Jesus at Cana was made in an instant of time but had the appearance of a well matured vintage wine. So it would be that if the rock when created already contained uranium and lead or potassium and argon, then by radiometric dating that rock would appear old despite being very young.

Meteorite Shower

In actual fact there are many other indicators of the age of the earth and solar system, and these, unfortunately for the evolutionist, give ages far below those generally accepted by them. A selection of these indicators will establish the fact of a young earth and solar system.

1.   **Interplanetary Dust.** Micrometeors in the Solar System are being dragged towards the sun constantly. If the Solar System **is** as old as the evolutionist says, there would be no more dust left. Indeed it would take only 2½ million years for the sun to sweep the Solar System clean. hence it is likely that the Solar System is less than 2½ million years old.

A Comet

2.   **Decay of the Tails of Comets.** It is known that comets are losing material all the time, from head to tail. For instance when Halley's comet last passed by the Earth in 1910 the rate of loss of mass was measured and found to be 30 tons/second. It has been shown that the rate of loss of mass is such that all the mass of comets would have been lost in less than 25,000 years.[2] This is another indication of a young solar system.

3.   **Influx of Meteoric Dust.** It has been reckoned that some 14.2 million tons of tiny meteorites fall to the surface of the Earth each year from the solar system. These are so slow moving that they do not burn up but settle on the surface in a fine dust shower. If we assume a uniform rate of build-up (and most evolutionists prefer uniformitarianism) then over the 4,600 million years of Earth time we should expect to have a mantle of dust 54' deep on the surface of the Earth (and also on the Moon). With the Earth we would expect this mantle to have been washed into the oceans to accumulate on the ocean floor and to add Nickel content to the sea water. On the moon we would expect to see this 54 foot mantle of dust in situ—yet it just isn't there. When the first manned moon-shot was landing on the moon the lunar module was handled with great care because a thick mantle of dust was expected. On landing it was seen to be less than ½ inch thick. At the present rate of influx this is a clear sign of how young the moon is. Furthermore the amount of nickel in seawater confirms this and gives an Earth age of only 8-9,000 years.

4.   **Rates of Erosion and Deposition.** Taken at the rather slow rates at which these are acting at the moment, they cannot have been in action for very long. Benjamin Allen in 'The Geological Age of the Mississippi River'[3] has said that the Mississippi delta can only be 5,000 years old at the maximum.

The river Niagara is presently cutting back into its bed at a rate of 3.8' per year. If this rate of erosion has been typical then the Niagara Upper Gorge is only 3,500 years old and not the very much larger age often given.

New   Stalactites!

At one time it was taught that stalactites and stalagmites took millions of years to form—now these ages have been reduced. A visit to any limestone cave where modern concrete entrances have been built is revealing. At the Dan-Yr-Ogof caves near Ystralfera in South Wales, there are stalactites 6 inches to 1 foot long hanging down from the concrete entrance which was built only a few years ago! The same can be seen on many modern buildings where limestone rock or cement has been used e.g. the Royal Festival Hall, London. The National

Geographic Magazine of October 1953[4] contained the picture of a bat encased in a stalactite—the bat shows no sign of decay, indicating that the stalactite encased it extremely rapidly and therefore grew extremely rapidly. Such rates of growth would require evidence of much longer stalactites and stalagmites to establish an earth as old as the evolutionists demand. The actual evidence is in fact consistent with a young earth.

5. **Moon quakes.** Since instruments have been landed on the moon certain surprising results have come from the data obtained. If the moon were as old as the supposed age of the earth, being a smaller body, it would by now have cooled completely and would be totally solid. A solid moon would not suffer from moonquakes. However the instruments have recorded several moonquakes, indicating a fluid core, and hence a young moon.

The evidence indicates that the moon is still cooling as it still radiates heat from its surface. Furthermore the existence of magnetic field suggests a fluid core. This too confirms that the moon is very much younger than its proclaimed 4.6 thousand million years.

6. **Population Growth.** If we assume that 2.5 children were born to every family, and that a new generation emerged every 43 years and the average life span (allowing for disease, famine and warfare through the ages) was 43 years, then the population would have reached its present level in only 6,000 years.

If the same figures are applied to a time span of one million years, the population would be so vast that the whole universe wouldn't be able to contain it (the number is 10^{2700} i.e. 10 followed by 2700 zeros).[5]

So we could go on. Dr. Henry Morris has listed up to 74 scientific checks[6] on how old the Earth is, which all show a young, and sometimes very young, Earth.

When the Bible is accepted literally, it too demands a young Earth. In Luke 3 a genealogy is given which shows a history from Adam right through to Christ, a time period of a few thousands years and no more. Some have said that this is simply a random list of selected individuals which is not supposed to be complete—yet when the genealogy in Genesis 5 is read it is clearly in language which demands that we take it as it is written e.g. Genesis 5: 6-8 'And Seth lived 105 years and begat Enos: and Seth lived after he begat Enos 807 years and begat sons and daughters; and all the days of Seth were 912 years and he died'. We are not only told the length of life, but how old he was when he had his son.

Such language is not figurative and it is obvious that these lists are either complete or lack only certain people whose sins exclude them from being named like those omitted from the genealogy in Matthew 1. Perhaps the Cainan of Luke 3 who is not mentioned in Genesis is one such person or perhaps he is a later addition to the Greek text. Such a case would be exceptional however. Creationists vary in their estimates of the age of the Earth, but on the basis of the lists in the Bible they **all** range from 6,000 to 14,000 years B.P. (before present) i.e. a Creation date between about 4,000 B.C. and 12,000 B.C.

If the Earth is young—even up to one million years—Evolution cannot have taken place by the processes suggested. This mass of evidence points to a young Earth and therefore a direct **Creative** act.

References:
1. Bolton Davidheiser *'Evolution and Christian Faith".* Presbyterian and Reformed Publishing Co. 1969.
2. R.A. Littleton *'Mysteries of the Solar System'.* Oxford, Clarendon Press, 1968. p.110.
3. Benjamin Allen *'The Geological Age of the Mississippi River'* Creation Research Society Quarterly IX September 1972.
4. National Geographic Magazine CIV (Oct. 1953)
5. Ed. Walter E. Lammerts *'Scientific Studies in Special Creation.'* Baker Book House, Grand Rapids, Michigan pp. 198-205.
6. Henry M. Morris *'The Young Earth'.* Creation Research Society Quarterly Vol. 12 No. 1. June 1975. p.21.

CHAPTER THREE

'Kinds'

When Charles Darwin studied at Cambridge, the generally held view was that there was an absolute fixity of species—in other words the animals and plants around were exactly the same in shape, colour and form as when they were first created. This was taken to be the Biblical view, and it was the view which Darwin's researches seemed to disprove. The crucial question for us is whether or not this is the view that the Bible gives.

Upon close inspection, it is quite clear that the bible does not hold to an absolute fixity of species. In Genesis 1 the picture given is of the Creation of various groupings called 'kinds'. These 'kinds' were categories of animals and plants so designed that they always produced animals or plants of their own 'kind'. Genesis 1: 11 and 12 'Then God said, Let the land produce vegetation: seed bearing plants and trees on the land that bear fruit with seed in it, according to their various kinds. And it was so. The land produced vegetation; plants bearing seed according to their kinds and trees bearing fruit with seed in it according to their kinds. And God saw that it was good.'
v. 20 and 21 'And God said, Let the water teem with living creatures, and let birds fly above the earth across the expanse of the sky.

So God created great creatures of the sea and every living thing and moving thing with which the water teems, according to their kinds, and every winged bird according to its kind. And God saw that it was good.'

v. 24 and 25 'And God said, Let the land produce living creatures according to their kinds: livestock, creatures that move along the ground, and wild animals, each according to its kind. And it was so. God made wild animals according to their kind, livestock acording to their kinds, and all the creatures that move along the ground according to their kinds. And God saw that it was good.'

Here then we have several categories in the initial creation. The restriction was that they could only reproduce within the confines of their own group, and that no group could produce offspring of another group although as we shall see, development within the kinds could occur.

This contrasts sharply with evolutionary theory which has all the present groups of animals developing from one common ancestral line i.e. unicellular organisms - multicellular organisms - invertebrates - vertebrates, fish - amphibians - reptiles - mammals - man. This scheme offers no restrictive boundaries to the developing species. So the evolutionary plan of development is seen as a tree having every branch originating from the same stem. Fish were the forefathers of the land creatures; reptiles evolved to birds; early primates gradually became men and so on.

The Biblical scheme on the other hand has many trees, each tree being called a 'kind'. So the cat family is one kind—it has many different types of cat within it but all the forms of cats can be traced back to the originally created cats. Cats will never produce non-cats—the **kind** is fixed. Variation and adaptation can occur within the kind but will never cross the 'kind' boundaries. So dogs didn't originate from the cat kind, dogs came from the dog kind. There are at present over 200 varieties of dog all capable of interbreeding but they are **all** dogs and always will be.

Any animals or plants which can together successfully produce offspring belong to the same kind automatically. Often the divergence has become so great within the kind that cross-breeding is no longer possible, but as a rule of thumb cross-breeding is a good indicator. A horse and an ass can cross-breed even though the resultant animal is infertile—so horses and asses belong to the same kind. Hens and turkeys also therefore belong to one kind and lions and tigers. Plants may also cross fertilize if they are of the same kind; for example citrus fruit trees, various grasses and even radishes and cabbages which both belong to the mustard family.

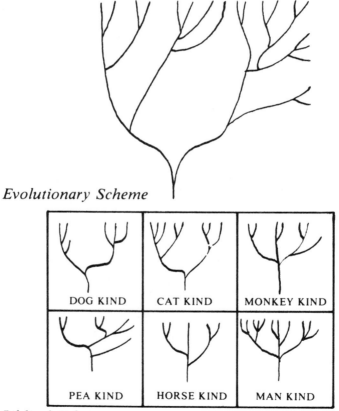

Evolutionary Scheme

| DOG KIND | CAT KIND | MONKEY KIND |
| PEA KIND | HORSE KIND | MAN KIND |

Biblical Scheme

The Bible therefore allows for MICROEVOLUTION or ADAPTATION, but does not allow for MACRO-EVOLUTION in which reptiles may become birds, or monkeys become men.

The fossil record is where we must look for the evidence. The Creationist expects to find evidence of the sudden emergence of distinct types with no signs of transition between them. What the evolutionist expects in the fossil record is evidence of gradual development and a sequence of increasing order and complexity with time. Unfortunately for the evolutionist this is not the case. The earliest rocks on earth, according to

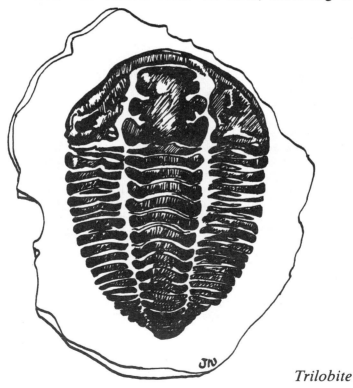

Trilobite

29

Geologists, are those which belong to the Pre-Cambrian Period. In these rocks not 'a single indisputable multicellular fossil has ever been found,'[1] and yet in the next group of rocks, the Cambrian, fossils of extremely complex organisms are found. They have appeared suddenly with no trace of any transitional forms. This contradicts the Evolutionary model, but wholly reinforces the Creationist model.

Many evolutionary books are honest about this problem. In 'Fossils in Colour' [2] Professor J. F. Kirkaldy says, 'The earliest known trilobites occur in rock of the Lower Cambrian Age. These are highly developed forms, but we have not a trace of their ancestors.' His explanation is that the ancestors 'must have been soft-bodied without any parts capable of fossilization.' This is startling for two reasons. Firstly, because earlier in his book he discusses the 'entirely soft-bodied' worms and talks of the fossils they have left in Cambrian rocks. Secondly, he is admitting that there are no transitional forms in the development of hard shells—the hard parts of the trilobites suddenly appeared!!

From this point in Geological time the same sudden appearance and lack of transitional forms characterizes the fossil record. Again evolutionists admit the difficulty. One of the greatest palaeontologists of recent years has said 'On still higher levels, in those of what is called here megaevolution, essentially continuous transitional sequences are not merely rare, but are virtually absent. Their absence is so nearly universal that it cannot off-hand be imputed entirely to chance.'[3]

Professor Corner, of Cambridge University says "I still think that **to the unprejudiced** the fossil record of plants is in favour of special creation.'[4] An amazing confession from one who is not a fundamentalist but a leading academic botanist. He says this because of the sudden appearance of fossil forms. Darwin found some fossils and expected that the transitional forms would eventually be found as the search for fossils continued—yet a hundred years on there are still no

Archaeopteryx — Bird or Reptile?

transitional forms. More and more fossils have been found, but instead of filling the known gaps they have produced still more gaps. Had evolutionary change occurred over vast aeons of time, transitional forms must have roamed earth for many millions of years, yet their fossils are strangely absent. **NOT ONE** fossil of an intermediate stage has yet been found. At one time it was thought that Archaeopteryx was such a form. Here was a fossil which had wings and feathers but which also had teeth and wing claws. Evolutionists at first proclaimed that the first transitional fossil had been discovered which was half bird and half reptile and which proved that birds had come from reptiles, a fact which they had stated formerly because the scales on the legs of hens had been seen as a remnant from reptilian days.

Today, however, as has been reaffirmed recently by a Yale professor, Archaeopteryx is seen as nothing but 100% bird and not a transitional form at all. The wing claws prove nothing as a South American bird called a Hoatzin (which no one would say is anything but a bird) also has wing claws when young. It is true that no present living birds have teeth but this doesn't mean that it was always so. Some fossil fish had teeth and some didn't; some fossil mammals had teeth and some didn't—so why must we assume that in the past some birds could not have had teeth? To add to this, a fossil 100% bird which the evolutionists say is much older than Archaeopteryx has now been found ending the whole discussion and putting Archaeopteryx definitely outside the class of a transitional form.

Horse fossils are often used as a classic example of evolutionary development beginning with the so called ancestor 'eohippus' and leading up to the present day forms of horse. The impression given by evolutionists is that this development is clear and gradual, and that intermediate forms are well attested by the fossil record. "In mammals, the gap between horses, asses and zebras[5] (genus Equus) and their closest living relatives . . . is filled by an extensive series of fossils." De Nony, however, admits that these forms "seem to have appeared 'suddenly' and it has not yet been possible because of the lack of fossils to reconstitute the passage between these intermediates, yet it must have existed"![6] Nowhere is there found a progression of horse fossils in one area; indeed nowhere is any part of the sequence found in successive rock layers. Both the fossils and their geographical locations are widely divergent.

Further disturbing aspects of detail are found in the supposed development of the horse if the fossil remains are linked together in an evolutionary sequence. Four toes become one toe, whilst the number of pairs of ribs go from 18 in Eohippus to 15 in Orohippus to 19 in Pliohippus and then back to 18 in Equus Scotti. The number of lumbar vertebrae vary from 6 or 7 in Eohippus to 8 in Orohippus and back to 6 in the modern horse![7] Where is the order in this? It is no wonder therefore that one writer stated, "Despite a great deal of antiquarian research and much ingenious speculation there remain a good many unsolved riddles connected with the origin and early history of the horse."[8]

Is it not possible that these fossil remains are those of animals which lived at the same time in the past and which today are extinct? The fact that the variety of horses is more limited today and that there may have been other types formerly says *nothing* about evolutionary development.

The basic error of evolutionists is their misinterpretation of what they see around them, and of the fossil record. They see the changes in the finches on the Galapagos Islands, they see the development of rats and mice resistant to known poisons, they see the minor changes in the Micraster fossils and they conclude that if these small changes occur for long enough an entirely new form will result. Darwin does exactly this in his opus magnum 'The Origin of Species'. But these micro-evolutionary changes show nothing of the sort. The finches were still finches, the rats and mice are still rats and mice, and after 20 million years(!) the micrasters of the chalk layers are

Micraster

still micrasters. The fossil changes that have emerged are on a small level only: indeed some of the changes can only be seen under a microscope. All that the text books on evolution do is to show examples of this minor adaptation.

This microevolution is not only a proven fact, it is what the Bible demands. Out from Noah came all the types of man found on the Earth today—his children and their wives were the 'genetic soup' out of which the Negroid, Mongoloid, Caucasian and other races sprang. Without this development all men would have the same colour, the same hair type and be of the same blood group. Is it not also possible that the Ark contained animals which were themselves genetic soups—that a pair of dogs were say the 'Noah' dogs from which came the Huskies, Chihuahuas, Alsatians, Pugs, Labradors and the Yorkshire terrier? This demands microevolution.

What is worse for the evolutionist is that certain supposedly extinct fossil creatures have been found alive and well on the Earth. These creatures make the evolutionists feel uncomfortable for two reasons—firstly according to them these creatures disappeared as fossils hundreds of millions of years ago. Secondly when they reappear they are instantly recognizable, meaning that not one bone or scale has evolved in any way. A proof of non-evolution if anything.

A fish called the Coelacanth was at first proclaimed as a transitional fossil. It was said to have lived millions of years ago, becoming extinct about 70 million years ago and to have been the forerunner of the fish which eventually led to air-breathing land animals. Unfortunately for the evolutionist however, a perfect living Coelacanth was landed in the nets of fishermen off Madagascar in 1938—the first of many to be caught—and *it* hadn't changed one scale! The Coelacanth is now said by evolutionists to be unusual in that it didn't evolve!

So also the Tuatara, a reptile living in New Zealand today was last identified as a 135 million year old fossil.

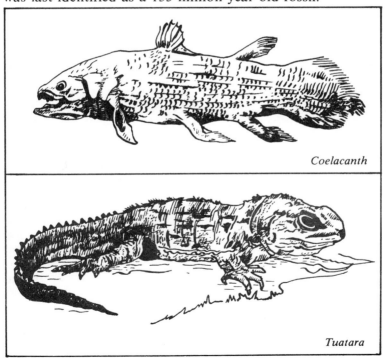

Coelacanth

Tuatara

How grateful we should be that the duckbilled platypus is still with us; the evolutionists would really have claimed it as the final proof had it only been evidenced as a fossil—'link between birds and mammals at last established' would have been their cry. Actually it is not a transitional form, but a full complex member of the Monotreme family.

Duck-billed Platypus

More on the fossil record will be considered later but let us complete this section with a resumé.

Evolution demands a scheme which would show simple cells gradually developing and increasing in complexity with transitional forms in abundance between the fossil types.

The Biblical scheme would expect the sudden appearance of complex organisms and no transitional forms.

On the evidence available it must be said that the fossil record strongly supports the Biblical rather than the Evolutionary scheme.

References:
1. Duane T. Gish *'Evolution — The fossils say NO!'* Creation Life Publishers p.45. 1976.
2. Professor John F. Kirkaldy *'Fossils in Colour'*. Blandford Press, London. 4th Edition 1975.
3. G.G. Simpson *'Tempo and Mode in Evolution'*. Columbia University Press, New York (1944) pp.105-106.
4. E.J.H. Corner *'Contemporary Botanical Thought'*. A.M. MacLeod & L.S. Cobley Eds., Quadrangle Books, Chicago. 1961.
5. Colin Patterson *'Evolution'*. British Museum (Natural History), London. 1978.
6. L. Du Nouy *'Human Destiny'*. New American Library, New York. p.74 (1947).
7. C.E.A. Turner *'Horse Evolution'*. Pamphlet No. 74 (New Edition) — Evolution Protest Movement. June 1973.
8. Professor J.A.S. Watson. Encyclopaedia Britannica 1950 Vol. 11 p.754.

CHAPTER FOUR

The Geology of the Earth's Surface

A further evolutionary system of working out the age of the Earth leads us on to study what is called the Geological table. Geologists have attempted to estimate the age of the Earth from the rates at which sediments are deposited. They can measure rates of accumulation around the Earth today and so establish an average figure for the rate of deposition. They assume that this deposition has occurred at a uniform rate throughout geological history (quite an assumption!) and so work out how long it has taken for any given layer of rock to have been laid down.

For example, it has been calculated[1] that one foot of sediment is deposited every 2,000 years—so in any given area, a 1,000' deep stratum of rock would have taken two million years to be deposited. This is the manner in which the absolute duration of deposition is worked out by evolutionary geologists.

Having then estimated the period of formation, the Geologist then wants to know the sequence in which the rock layers were laid down. If all the rock layers in the world were without exception in the same order, it would be easy. The rule would then be that the upper rocks must be younger because they were laid down on top of the rocks beneath viz:-

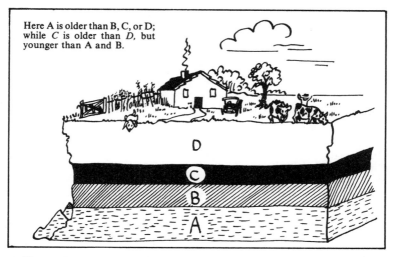

Here A is older than B, C, or D; while *C* is older than *D*, but younger than A and B.

How then was the rock sequence now accepted by most Geologists established? Giovanni Pinna on p. 10 of his book 'The Dawn of Life'[2] explains it very simply, 'In geology where time is measured in millions of years there are two ways of dating rocks: one is the absolute method which establishes exactly the number of years elapsed since their formation by radiometric and other tests, and the other is the relative method which determines only whether a rock is older than, contemporary with, or more recent than, another. This last system is based on the concept that each epoch of the Earth's history has had characteristic animal and vegetable types . . . and *on the basis of a study of fossils* deducing the position that they occupied in geological time and the age of the rock that contains them.' (Author's emphasis)

Now here is the most striking example of cyclic reasoning. The fossils are assumed to have become more complex because they have evolved, and on that assumption the presence of complex animal remains in a rock layer is said to show that it is of a more recent origin. Once the relative age is established, the increasing complexity of fossils is then used to demonstrate the course of evolution! Often a fossil is found which is said to be indicative of a certain age of rock and is called the INDEX fossil, which is then used to identify the age of that rock. One example of an INDEX fossil is a certain type of Trilobite which is said to have lived only in the Cambrian—any rock in which it is found is thus said to be Cambrian. This order of rocks, established by the fossils, is then used to demonstrate Evolution, i.e. fossils establish the relative age of the rocks—and the age of the rocks date the fossils! Even the Encyclopaedia Brit.[3] 1973 Ed. Vol. 7 p. 850 says, 'As is well known the order of geological strata is fixed entirely by means of fossils.' Similarly in Vol 20 'Because of the fossils entombed in them the sedimentary rocks contain the whole of the life-record of the past. And by means of their fossil content they can be arranged in a chronological order.' Thus the geological method *presumes* the existence in these periods of living beings of gradually increasing complexity.

The Coelacanth has upset this system because before it was found alive off Madagascar its fossils were used as an INDEX fossil of the ages occurring between 280 million and 70 million years during which periods it was said to have flourised and then become extinct. Yet the fact that it still lives shows that if the geologists are correct it must also have lived in the succeeding ages yet apparently without leaving any trace of its existence.

However, using this system of fossil chronology, two geologists Hutton and Lyell worked out the following table. It must be stated again that the table assumes two things: 1. An evolution of species and therefore an observable increase in the complexity of fossils; and 2. A uniform undisturbed rate of deposition. It is the latter assumption of a uniform rate of deposition that has given the name UNIFORMITARIAN-ISM to this system.

THE GEOLOGICAL TABLE

Name	Duration
HOLOCENE	10,000 years
PLEISTOCENE	1 million years
PLIOCENE	10 million years
MIOCENE	14 million years
OLIGOCENE	15 million years
EOCENE	30 million years
CRETACEOUS	65 million years
JURASSIC	45 million years
TRIASSIC	45 million years
PERMIAN	45 million years
CARBONIFEROUS	80 million years
DEVONIAN	50 million years
SILURIAN	40 million years
ORDOVICIAN	60 million years
CAMBRIAN	600 million years
PRE-CAMBRIAN	?? million years

The American system is the same except that the Carboniferous is divided into two parts called the Mississippian (the older) and the Pennsylvanian.

PENNSYLVANIAN
MISSISSIPPIAN

This order has never been found in its entirety and in many areas the rock layers are completely at variance with it. Once the table was established, however, it gradually assumed the status of fact and now geologists no longer test the theory by the finds, but instead, where the finds disagree with the table they seek alternative explanations of the data.

There are several things which cause the Uniformitarian geologist problems, for example Missing strata, and Strata and fossils in the wrong order.

1. Missing Strata
Often when considering the rock strata the order is found to be incomplete.

F	
E	F
D	E
C	B
B	A
A	
Expected layers	Layers found by field-research

The usual explanation is that erosion has occurred removing layers C and D and deposition has continued immediately afterwards leaving layer E on layer B.

i.e.

Before

D
C
B
A

After Erosion

B
A

After Continued
Deposition

F
E
B
A

The problem is that often there is no evidence for such erosion and it is clear that often the layers have been deposited directly on top of one another in a straight sequence. The Grand Canyon is one mile deep and shows very clearly the succession of strata—an undisturbed pattern with no signs of erosion.[4] Yet it does not show the complete pattern as given in the Geological Table. Certain strata are missing—for example the Permian fossils rest directly upon the Mississippian—and worse still the Mississippian rocks rest directly on the Cambrian so that there are no Ordovician, Silurian or Devonian rocks. This huge gap was apparently the result of millions of years of erosion—erosion for which there is no visible evidence. The great geologist Suess[5] said that this was 'cause for astonishment'. An understatement indeed!

More difficult for the geologist is the situation where a rock sequence is repeated many times in the same order—for example in the Highlands of Scotland where the following order is repeated five times.

B	
A	
B	
A	
B	
A	
B	
A	
B	*Sandstones and Limestone*
A	*Gneiss and Schists*
B	
A	

The fossil order
is repeated
similarly.

2. Strata in the Wrong Order

This occurs in many areas where the older strata given in the Geological Table are at the tops of mountains with the so called 'younger' rocks underneath.[6] There are hundreds of examples of these and each one has to be explained. For example:- In one 7,000 square mile area of Montana, Alberta and British Columbia the Rocky Mountains show Precambrian and Cambrian rocks at the top, with a layer of Cretaceous rocks below!![7] In the Heart Mountain area of Wyoming, U.S.A. Ordovician, Devonian and Mississippian rocks rest horizontally on Eocene beds[8] (see Geological Table p.2 to see how wrong this must be).

It is here that geologists use various devices to explain what is found. They use two methods (a) Overfolds, and (b) Thrusting.

Overfolds
Overfolds are drawn in every physical geography text book—they come in two forms as shown:-

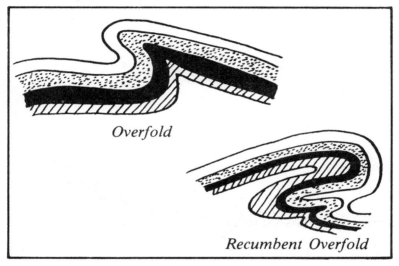

Overfold

Recumbent Overfold

How often have geography students wondered how such vast folding of solid rock could have occurred without shattering the rock to pieces. Often such structures are simply invented to explain what is found. The following diagram is found in Monkhouse[9] 'Principles of Physical Geography' p. 37

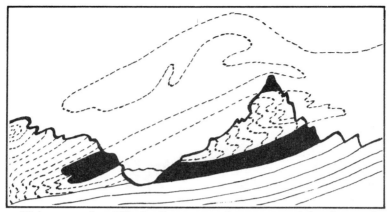

This oversimplified diagram tries to explain how the observed strata could exist. Yet the rock shown is all sedimentary i.e. deposited rock. Were it from a volcano it would be easy to understand how such a flow could come about, but how does solid rock form such patterns without signs of shattering or friction? Besides, it is unprovable that such a pattern existed at all, although diagrammatically it is very convenient.

Thrusting

Here a recumbent overfold is said to have sheered off because of continued great pressure and moved a great distance along the ground i.e. a nappe.

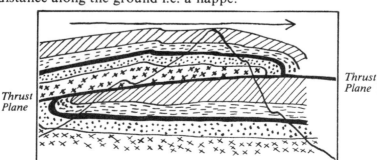

In the diagram the strata are in the wrong order, so an overthrust is used to explain it.

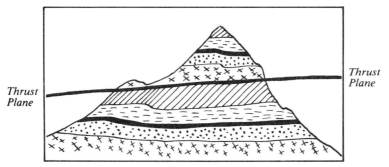

Again very convenient—but where thrusting *has* generally occurred (and it definitely has to a limited extent in some areas) the friction between the two rock surfaces has been so great that scratching has been found with finely ground debris between the two rock faces—signs of definite movement. In most features thus explained, however, there is no such evidence.

Also it has been found that there is a definite limit to the size of block which can be thrusted, and that if this size is exceeded it shatters into many fragments. Yet many of the claimed examples of thrusting exceed this size by many times e.g. The Lewis overthrust is said to be 350 miles wide, 6 miles deep and displaced by 35 miles. Some even claim that part of North Africa moved north and finally right over Switzerland to form the Alps!

Actually to the unprejudiced observer there are many other features found 'in the field' that are not explained by the geological column and uniformitarianism. Let us begin with the questions we have all asked ourselves at times:- For example, How do leaves get perfectly preserved in lumps of coal when coal is formed of decaying vegetation? Why didn't the leaf decay? How were the animal tracks in sand preserved? What about the mammoths?

Coal. It is said by UNIFORMITARIANS that coal seams are the result of forests growing in bogs. Leaves fall from the trees, and the dead leaves fall themselves into the shallow water and begin decaying. They are then covered with succeeding layers and gradually become compressed before the decomposition becomes complete. The problem is that leaves in perfect condition, even with the colour preserved, are often found in coal somehow having resisted the decay. And not only vegetation but cockroaches, dragonflies and spiders are all perfectly preserved. Both the vegetation and insect life show that the familiar forms were all much larger than they are today—very tall trees; ferns sometimes 50 feet high; and dragonflies having a wing-span of over one foot. These are explained in terms of tropical conditions which existed in N.W. Europe, Northern China, North America and Antarctica where the major coal deposits are now found.

Leaf Preserved in Coal

More disturbing even than this is the fact that upright tree trunks have been found cutting through several layers of coal. These are called POLYSTRATE trees. The coal seams apparently took up to 50 million years to form and yet one tree grew through it all!!! During this 50 million years the vegetation must also have remained the same because the same plant and insect forms which are found at the top of the seams are found at the bottom.

Polystrate Fossil Tree

Tracks. Any one who lives by the sea and walks along the sandy shore is used to seeing tracks being formed. Close observation shows also that these tracks don't last very long — usually minutes or even seconds. Yet when fossil tracks appear in the rocks it is claimed that an animal walked over the area and that the tracks were preserved despite the action of wind and water. Surely something extraordinary would have been necessary to preserve them, for example an inundation by mud or volcanic lava.

Dinosaur Footprints

A Mammoth

The Mammoths. Among the animals known to have existed in the past, few have created as many problems as the mammoth. These 8 ton animals which were slightly smaller than present day elephants are not found alive on the Earth today, but are found perfectly preserved in the permafrost (layers which are permanently frozen) of the whole of Northern Russia and Siberia. Many have been found upright in deep frozen mud with undigested vegetation in their mouths and stomachs. The flesh is so fresh that explorers' dogs have been fed on it in emergencies, and the ivory, which like the flesh, decays very easily, is also found in perfect condition and has been widely available on the world market. An analysis of the Mammoths' stomach contents shows that the vegetation of their time was warm-weather vegetation, and because like today's elephants they lacked sebaceous glands they too must have been warm climate animals. It is usually taught that these mammoths were feeding on a muddy river bank and fell into the mud becoming asphyxiated in the process. This, however,

50

does not explain the amazing preservation. A dead animal begins decaying within hours of death: so for the mammoths to be found in such a good state of preservation can only mean that they died and were frozen within a matter of hours. This is a major problem because they are found in all depths of mud sometimes 900 feet deep. What is it that could bury thousands of mammoths in 900 feet of mud, and freeze them all solid in hours? Uniformitarianism cannot answer the problem.

There are problems on a smaller scale which are just as puzzling. Dr. Clifford Burdick[10] has found pine and other pollens in all the layers exposed in the Grand Canyon from the Cambrian upwards, which would show that pine trees and others were growing and fully developed in those times! Burdick says that, "The discovery of both Gymnosperm and Angiosperm pollen grains in the Cambrian and Pre-Cambrian (ca 500 million years ago) does indeed present problems. A parallel situation in the animal kingdom would be the location of mammals in the Pre-Cambrian . . . finding the spores of plants at least closely related to pines in the Pre-Cambrian makes it extremely difficult to visualize any evolutionary development of these specialized plants."

As well as these problems there are other more unusual ones. A metal vase with a silver design of flowers on the outside was found in solid rock at Dorchester, Massachusetts in 1851[11] by quarrymen:- the rock was said by geologists to be millions years old. How did the vase get into it?

In 1885 at Vocklabruck, Austria[12] a block of coal (said to be 50-300 million years old) broke open and a metal cube was found inside. Upon examination it was found to have been manufactured, and it had a deep groove all the way round it.

In 1889 a man drilling for water in Idaho[13] found a baked clay figure 1½″ in length at a depth of 300 feet in solid rock said to be 10 million years old. In 1891 a woman in Illinois[14] broke a large piece of coal open and found a manufactured gold chain in it, with the ends still embedded in the coal.

And so the stories carry on. How can rocks millions and millions of years old contain such things when the rocks have been undisturbed, and when man was, according to evolutionary theory not even a twinkle in 'Nature's' eye. Something is wrong!

And not only these—fossil human tracks[15] have been found. In Utah, adult and baby human tracks have been found in Cambrian rocks; in one instance footprints made by manufactured shoes have been found in Cambrian rocks, and one has the imprint of a trilobite (which is an index fossil for the Cambrian rocks) in the heel!

These and many more are factual finds—they must be ignored as if they did not exist, explained away, or there must be a fundamental reassessment of the scheme of geological succession.

What answers then does the Creationist picture have to these enigmas?

References:

1. Schuchart's work quoted in a Paper entitled 'Flood Geology' given by Brian Newton at the 'Bible-Science' Conference held at Swanwick, Derbyshire in 1975.

2. Giovanni Pinna *'The Dawn of Life'*. Orbis Publishing, London 1972.

3. Encyclopaedia Britannica Vol. 7 p.850. Vol 20 p.156. 1973.

4. Richard M. Field *'The Principles of Historical Geology'*. Princeton University Press 1933 p.194. and quoted by Clifford Burdick in his article *'Streamlining Stratigraphy'* in *'Scientific Studies in Special Creation'* Ed. Walter E. Lammerts. Baker Book House, Grand Rapids, Michigan.

5. Edward Suess *'The Face of the Earth'*. 2:543.

6. Clifford Burdick *'Microflora of the Grand Canyon'*. Creation Research Society Quarterly 111 June 1966 pp.38 - 50.

7. Byron C. Nelson *'The Deluge Story in Stone'*. Bethany Fellowship Inc. Publishers, Minneapolis, Minnesota.

8. Whitcomb and Morris *'The Genesis Flood'*. Baker Book House, Grand Rapids, Michigan, p.181. 1961.

9. F.J. Monkhouse *'Principles of Physical Geography'. 4th Edition 1965.*

10. Clifford Burdick *'Microflora of the Grand Canyon'*. Creation Research Society Quarterly 111 June 1966 pp.38-50.

11. Scientific American Vol. 7 p.298.

12. Quoted by Erich Von Fange *'Time Upside Down'*. Creation Research Society Quarterly Vol. 11 No.1 June 1974 p.16

13. Quoted by George Mulfinger *'A Unique Creationist Exhibit'*. Creation Research Society Quarterly Vol. 10 No.1 June 1973 pp.62 - 63.

14. Quoted by George Mulfinger *'A Unique Creationist Exhibit'*. Creation Research Society Quarterly Vol. 10 No.1 June 1973 p.65.

15. A.G. Ingalls *'The Carboniferous Mystery'*. Scientific American Vol. 162 p14 Jan. 1940.

CHAPTER FIVE

A Catastrophe

The Bible presents a picture of CATASTROPHE. A few thousand years after the Creation of the Earth and the life forms on it, Genesis says that a major disaster occurred. A Flood of Universal extent and proportions overwhelmed the whole Earth and destroyed all life with the exception of the eight human beings and the animal kinds preserved in the Ark.

Where did the water come from? The answer is given again in the first chapter of Genesis where we read in verses 6, 7 & 8 'And God said "Let there be an expanse between the waters to separate water from water". So God made the expanse and separated the water under the expanse from the water above it. And it was so. God called the expanse 'sky'.'

Before this second day vast amounts of water covered the surface of the Earth. Here this water is split into two parts—one part which remained on the Earth's surface, and one part which encircled the Earth, probably in the form of a belt of water vapour.

When Noah's Flood came, Genesis says "all the springs of the great deep burst forth, and the floodgates of the heavens were opened." 'The springs of the great deep' may refer to underground areas of water storage, the remains of which may perhaps be seen in the deep oceanic trenches; or they may refer to volcanic action and crustal disturbances. 'The floodgates of the heavens' almost certainly refer to the water canopy.

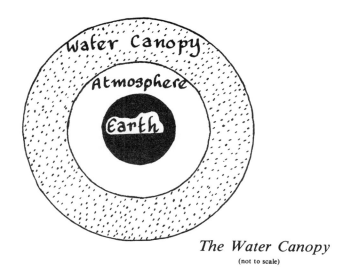

The Water Canopy
(not to scale)

But what effect would such a water vapour belt have on the Earth?

The first effect would be a climatological one. It is a well known fact that the Earth's atmosphere does not heat up directly from the sun but from the Earth's re-radiation of the sun's rays.

As the sun's rays enter the Earth's atmosphere they pass through without being absorbed. When they reach the Earth's surface they are then absorbed and heat up the ground. Once heated up, the ground re-radiates the heat at a different wavelength which the atmosphere can then absorb. This is the reason why in summer, although the sun's rays are hottest at midday, the hottest time of the day isn't until 2 or 3 o'clock in the afternoon—this delay being the time it takes for the atmosphere to heat up.

55

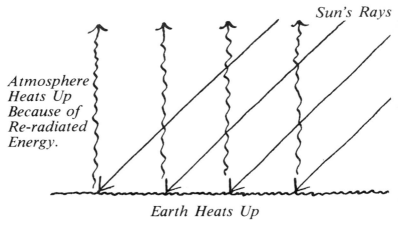

Earth Heats Up

Re-radiation of Solar Energy by the Earth

This re-radiated energy then either returns into space or meets clouds which in turn absorb the energy and radiate the heat back down to the Earth. In winter months a cloudless sky on a cold night will mean a heavy frost because the re-radiated energy is lost. But should a cloud cover develop, frost becomes extremely unlikely because of this so-called 'Greenhouse Effect'.

So the belt of water vapour which existed before Noah's Flood would have trapped heat in the Atmosphere. It is likely therefore that temperatures generally would have been higher than they are now and would therefore account for the tropical **conditions leading to the larger plants, insects and animals** shown in the fossil record.

Another important factor is that the water vapour would **also have redistributed the sun's heat throughout the Earth** meaning that the climate would probably have been the same on the Equator as at the Poles. Hence the mammoths would easily have been able to exist and eat sub-tropical plants even in Northern Siberia. There would have been no ice caps in Antarctica where the sub-tropical plants found fossilized in the coal deposits would have grown naturally.

Such a uniformity of temperature would have meant that high and low pressures would not have formed and therefore there would have been no strong winds, no evaporation (no clouds), no rain and no ocean currents. There would also be no variation in temperature between the top and bottom of mountains and so no local winds. Furthermore, climatic changes such as cold winters and hot summers would not have existed on the Earth.

Here then was a uniform climate. This is the only explanation of the problem that has confronted geologists studying coal deposits—namely why the trees forming the coal show no annual rings of growth.[1] That there would have been no rain is perfectly borne out by Genesis 2: 5 and 6 'for the Lord God had not sent rain upon the earth . . . but streams came up from the earth and watered the whole surface of the ground'. These undoubtedly fed the antidiluvian river system. Under these ideal conditions man's technological advance would have been very rapid and it may be that Noah and his ancestors were far more advanced in every sphere than we give them credit for.

Two other effects of the water canopy should also be mentioned—they are both related to the fact that a water vapour canopy would absorb much of the cosmic radiation entering the Earth's atmosphere.

The first of these is the effect on ageing. The antediluvian inhabitants of the Earth lived much longer than men do now. Indeed the Genesis record shows this longevity up to Noah when all but Enoch lived for about 800 or 900 years. Yet after the flood, life spans were dramatically reduced.

The second effect would have been upon the production of C^{14}.

Radio Carbon Dating

The basic system of radio carbon dating works as follows:-
(a) Cosmic radiation reaching the earth's upper atmosphere transmutes the nitrogen into the radioactive isotope of Carbon called C^{14}.
(b) This C^{14} oxidizes to form Carbon dioxide.
(c) This Carbon dioxide with its radio carbon component is absorbed by plants which are in turn eaten by living creatures which also absorb the C^{14}. It is also dissolved in the oceans in which other organisms live.

(d) Upon death, plants and animals absorb no more C^{14} and the C^{14} already absorbed begins to decay at a known rate. All plants and animals therefore contain proportions of C^{14} and non-radioactive carbon (C^{12}). After death the C^{14} decreases and the proportion of ordinary carbon therefore increases.

(e) By measuring the proportion of C^{14} left in dead creatures and comparing it with the proportion of C^{14} in living creatures the time of death can be worked out.

This is a very neat method of ascertaining more recent dates, but it too is fraught with problems. If a water canopy existed before the Flood the resultant reduced radiation would mean that very little C^{14} would have been produced and so the animals and plants living at that time would have very little C^{14} in them. After their death the amount of C^{14} would decrease still further with the result that a researcher finding them today would measure the proportion of C^{14} present and find it very low. His mistaken conclusion would be that the creature is much older than it really is.

A readjustment would appear approximately thus.

Conventional Radiocarbon Methods (in years)	Corrected Methods (after Charles Clough) [2] (in years)
40,000+	10,000
25,000	7,000
10,000	5,500
5,000	4,500

With this correction, dating of the remains of once living organisms comes within the scope of Biblical Chronology.

Another factor of inaccuracy involves the rapid decay which is occurring in the Earth's magnetic field. Dr. Thomas G. Barnes[3] has said that it loses half its strength every 1,400 years. So in 2222 B.C. it was 8 times stronger than today; in 822 B.C. it was 4 times stronger; in 579 A.D. it was twice as strong. As it becomes weaker, less cosmic radiation is reflected and greater amounts enter the Earth's atmosphere to form more C^{14}. A correction for this would further shorten the measured ages.

Other inaccuracies are also present. M. A. Cook cites the case of molluscs living in warm, alkaline waters which had a reduced amount of C^{14} in them—so much so in fact that a C^{14} test showed the living molluscs to have been dead 1,000 to 2,300 years!!![4]

So we see that adjustments have to be made in C^{14} dates to allow for the Genesis water canopy and the inaccuracies of the method.

The Flood
When the Flood hit the Earth dramatic worldwide changes occurred. We are told in Genesis 7: 12 that it rained for 40 days and 40 nights. This rain would have been even more violent and powerful than the Monsoons of Asia are today—for in 40 days sufficient water had poured down on the Earth to cover the highest mountain of those days. It is likely for reasons which we will examine later that the mountains were not as high as today, but they were all covered to a depth of over 20 feet. Genesis 7: 18, 19 and 20 says, 'The waters rose and increased greatly on the earth; and the ark floated on the surface of the water. They rose greatly on the earth, and all the high mountains under the entire heavens were covered. The waters rose and covered the mountains to a depth of more than twenty feet.' Twenty feet is about half the height of the Ark which means that the Ark would have had freedom of movement over the highest hills.

Over a forty day period the waters rose on the Earth. This lapse of time is crucial for it would have meant a gradual inundation of the land by the water. We can imagine that the more mobile animals would head inland and into highland areas in an attempt to avoid the flood waters, and the effect of this would be a zoning in the animal life destroyed. The shore dwelling animals (amphibians) would be the first inundated. Those who could perhaps move some distance awkwardly inland (reptiles) would be next and so on until the very mobile mammals would be left on hill-tops to succumb last of all.

This would give us some zoning of the remains BUT there would be areas where animals would have been stranded together and where the remains would therefore be found mixed up. Tracks of fleeing animals could easily be left as a permanent record in areas where there was crustal instability and therefore volcanic action as the Flood was occurring, or where silt had infilled the tracks soon after they were made. At this time water, wind, earthquakes and volcanoes would have been active together.

The effects of such a concentration of forces would have been to reshape the surface of the earth through massive movement of the earth's crust. The simple marine creatures and fish of the ocean floor oozes would be flattened and compressed; the muds and sands of the shores would be laid on top and so on.

It is very interesting that the fossils generally show the animals in unusual positions. If the evolutionists' view is correct and the fish and insects, for example, died and were gradually covered up, then it does not explain why the fossils of fish generally have their fins extended as if they had been swimming. A sudden inundation, however, would give just such a picture. Fish would be fleeing from the enormous waves, but would be flattened mid-course by the mud contained in the waves. Insects would also be flattened in flight by the wave of water and sediment cascading over the land.

60

Fossilized Fish

In other areas the remains of fish are twisted and distorted suggesting that a major catastrophe was the cause. In the Old Red Sandstone of Scotland, millions of fish are seen to have perished 'in alarm and agony'.[5] And again fossil graveyards have been identified e.g. the Karroo of South Africa, where thousands of millions of fossil remains are found together. In some areas animals which today are prey and predator are found in caves, perhaps sheltering together from some disaster. In other words the fossil evidence supports a catastrophic inundation of the Earth's surface by water.

In the picture of the Flood we find the answer to the problem of the frozen mammoths. The waves would easily have been able to cover them all with a thick mud deposit in such a way that mammoths would be found throughout the layer. It would explain why the mammoths died often with their mouths full of food—obviously surprised—and it also provides us with the answer to the greatest puzzle of all—how they were frozen solid within hours.

It is probable that the movement and headward rush of a wave of water perhaps several thousand feet high would greatly disturb the atmosphere: creating high pressure in front of it, and a marked low pressure behind it. Into this low pressure would be dragged a mass of freezing air sufficient to cause the type of instant chilling needed.

In Siberia, the land has remained frozen since the Flood and so the remains of frozen animals and plants can still be found. Elsewhere a similar freezing probably occurred but in the post-diluvian thaw the remains have vanished.

It is in this way and, many believe in this way only, that the fossil record makes sense. The formation of fossils requires special and extra-ordinary conditions. 'Under normal conditions such remains are not preserved at all. The body of an animal which has died in the open is usually quickly destroyed by scavengers, bacterial decomposition and the effects of sun, rain and frost. The preservation of animal remains, subsequently to become fossils, occurs only where the decomposition of the bones is prevented, as sometimes happens when a carcass is quickly buried and sealed from the atmosphere in the deposits of a marsh or lake.[6] The Noahian Flood provides the necessary mechanics and means for a worldwide production of fossils and for us it means that the majority of fossil remains found anywhere in the world today are linked directly to the events described in Genesis 7. As fossil remains are found at the tops of the major mountain blocks e.g. the Alps, the Himalayas, the Rockies and the Andes, the rocks now found at the top of such peaks must have been laid down during the Flood on top of the existing lower structures and the fossils in them must therefore be the remains of animals alive before the Flood. What it also shows is that the Flood period was typified by major mountain building with the associated vulcanicity and faulting. Vast lava flows found today may date from this time, e.g. The Columbia-Snake Plateau, U.S.A. which covers 250,000 square miles. If present day local floods can seriously alter the whole configuration of landscape and river patterns as shown with the example of East and West Lyn in North Devon in 1952, then the chiselling and remodelling effect of a vast worldwide Flood must not be underestimated.

Coal

If the idea of a gradual decay of vegetation being involved in the formation of coal has problems associated with it, what alternative does the Creationist put forward? To the Creationist the need for millions of years in the formation of coal deposits is unproven. There is in the coal industry a law called 'Hilt's Law'[7] which shows that the deeper the coal is found in the ground, the higher its grade—so that peat and brown coal (Lignite) are found near the surface, while anthracite is found at the lowest levels.

This suggests that the formation of coal occurs when wood is compressed very greatly without losing the heat formed by the compression. The result is that a metamorphosis of the wood occurs with coal as the end product—greater compression resulting in more complete metamorphosis. Certainly coal has been made from wood in the laboratory by this method in only a few hours.[8] Alternatively, surface vulcanicity may have set the vast forests on fire, carbonizing them before they were extinguished and buried.

In some areas the vegetation may well have been entirely uprooted and washed en masse to different locations, there to be laid in layers and covered over with shale and silt. The next wave would repeat the process and continue until no more vegetation was left. This would give the oft repeated pattern of coal, shale and silt so common in the world. And it would explain how certain leaves were preserved intact and perfect.

Oil may have been similarly formed except that animal remains rather than vegetation would have been involved in the metamorphosis. In Chemical and Engineering News[9], an experiment is described in which oil was made from manure in twenty minutes. So much for the need to have millions of years!

The Ice Age
To complete this section and introduce the next, the question of the Ice Age must be considered. Geographers have long argued about the number and the duration of ice advances and whereas most geography students learn that there were four advances—the Mindel, Riss, Wurm and Gunz—there is much opposition to this view. One geographer has even proposed as many as 27. The difficulty is that as a new ice sheet sweeps forward it removes the evidence left by any others, so who can be certain?

One fact which is fairly well-known is that it is very difficult with present physical and meteorological knowledge to explain how an Ice Age with an ice sheet advance could have been caused. For the huge amounts of ice involved in an advance, cold temperatures *and* large amounts of precipitation (snow, sleet and hail) are needed together. But in practice these work against one another.

When the air temperature plummets there is a very great reduction in evaporation. This in turn limits the quantity of moisture entering the atmosphere which consequently reduces the amount of snow which falls. This results in cold conditions but limited snowfall and therefore no ice advance.

On the other hand large snowfall results from a heavy cloud cover. This would prevent the sun's rays from reaching the Earth, reducing the rate of evaporation and thereby the snowfall. The result again is no ice advance.

Yet Geographers lead us to believe that cold temperatures *and* vast precipitation could occur together; but they fail to say how this could occur without a major catastrophe being involved.

The Flood, however, provides both the humidity and the freezing temperatures needed for the Ice Advance. The collapse of the Canopy and the resultant freezing down-draught of air would have cooled the Earth and produced the vast Ice sheets known to have covered the Northern parts of North America and Europe.

References:
1. Wilfred Francis *'Coal: Its Formation and Composition'*, 2nd ed., London: Edward Arnold Ltd., 1961 pp. ii, 625.
2. Taken from *'Laying the Foundation'*. 1977 A Framework for Basic Christian Doctrine by Dr. C. A. Clough. Produced by Lubbock Bible Church p.101.
3. Dr. Thomas G. Barnes, as quoted by the Rev. James C. Brady in his tract *'No Time for Evolution'*. distributed by Dr. A.J. Monty White, 19, Kidwelly Court, Hendredenny Park, Caerphilly, Mid Glamorgan, Wales.
4. M.A. Cook *Prehistory and Earth Models'*. Max Parish & Co. Ltd. 1966 p.4.
5. Hugh Miller *'The ORS'*. Everymans 1850.
6. *'Fossils in Caves'* Palaentology Leaflet No. 4. Natural History Museum 1974.
7. Melvin A. Cook *'Formation and Dating of Oil and Coal Deposits'*. 1970. Bible Science Newsletter VIII: 1st January 1970 p.1. and quoted by Morris, Boardman and Koontz in *'Science and Creation'*. A Handbook for Teachers. Creation-Science Research Centre, San Diego California 1971.
8. Chemical Tech. May 1972 p.276.
9. Chemical and Engineering News May 29, 1972, p.14.

CHAPTER SIX

Before and After

The changes that became apparent to Noah and the other seven people in the Ark when they re-emerged after their year long voyage, was remarkable. For 600 years Noah had lived in a world which was settled and which changed little from day to day.

The water vapour canopy meant that every day the temperatures were remarkably uniform, dipping only slightly during the night. The air was dry and motionless—it never rained, was never cloudy and was never windy. The rivers flowed gently to the sea which itself had no violent storms, just a gently rising and falling tide.

The life on the Earth was abundant and teeming. The trees reached hundreds of feet into the air—they grew all the year round and were capped and surrounded by vast canopies of leaves. The plants were large and constantly in bud, flower and fruit—agriculture was bountiful and the Earth was swathed with produce. Men and animals were long-living and strong.

The pre-Flood insect and animal life shown to us by the fossil evidence indicates how much larger these were, and how abundant in number. In one area alone the number of fossil fish has been estimated at over 800 million. The plant food was so abundant and easily replaced that the herbivorous animals abounded and grew large. Because of this the omnivorous and carnivorous animals also abounded—prey was plentiful and the number of species many. Our Earth today would appear poorly stocked in comparison, and with the continuing extinction of animals year by year, the downward trend continues. Mammoths, woolly rhinoceroses, mastadons, sabre-toothed tigers roamed the Earth, and the many varieties of dinosaurs were also present in abundance.

Dinosaurs

The question of dinosaurs has long been one of debate. Schools and Universities have taught for many years that the now extinct dinosaurs were the ancestors of present day reptiles and birds—most of us learnt it as a fact and find a reassessment very difficult. We now easily accept that "the robin is the nearest living relative to the dinosaur". Yet it is obvious that the Bible account of a world deluge is correct then the fossils of the dinosaurs are simply the remains of part of the pre-Flood animal life that roamed the Earth's surface thousands, not millions of years ago.

Brontosaurus
Brachiosaurus
Stegosaurus
Trachodon
Struthiomimus
Compsognathus
Diplodocus
Tyrannosaurus
Triceratops

The dinosaurs like many of the other created kinds came in many wonderful shapes and sizes and were certainly some of the largest animals ever to have lived. One of the largest, the Brachiosaurus was 80 feet long, with his head 40 feet in the air and weighed an estimated 90 tons. It is interesting to note, however, that the present day Blue Whale would still surpass it in a size and weight competition. Some dinosaurs were plant-eaters (brontosaurus), some meat-eaters (tyrannosaurus), some were defenceless (trachodon), some were armoured all over (ankylosauros), some were highly mobile (struthiomimus), some were cumbersome (diplodocus), some as large as, and larger than double-decker buses and others as small as present day chickens (compsognathus). Their fossil remains, like any others, required more or less immediate burial to protect them from disintegration, and the fact that these remains exist suggest a deluge.

All over the U.S.A., fossil human footprints are found. In a revealing paper in 'Scientific American' (1940), Professor Ingalls names States all over America in which these fossil prints are found—'from Virginia and Pennsylvania through Kentucky, Illinois, Missouri and westward towards the Rocky Mountains'[1]. Some have undoubtedly been carved, but where they have been found in deeply buried strata this is impossible. Yet such is the character of the Theory of Evolution, that instead of this evidence being used to evaluate and test the theory, the data is either rejected or explained away simply because it doesn't fit in with the theory. C. S. Lewis says 'There is always hope if we keep an unsolved problem fairly in view; there's none if we pretend it's not there'.[2] Professor Ingalls admits that if these tracks are the tracks of dinosaurs and men, then 'the whole science of geology is so completely wrong that all geologists will resign their jobs and take up truck driving.' He then continues 'Hence, for the present at least, science rejects the attractive explanation that man made these mysterious prints in the mud of the Carboniferous Period with his feet.'

Yet the Creationist can accept these for what they are—a clear fossil record which shows that in opposition to the evolutionary scheme, dinosaurs were on the Earth with man before the Flood. There is no evidence that they attacked man and it is likely that they stayed in their own habitats. We take elephants, crocodiles and rhinoceroses for granted because we have become accustomed to them—so Adam and all the people down to Noah were more than used to dinosaurs co-existing with them.

Once the Flood warning came, Noah had the job of building an ark large enough to take on board his own family plus a representation of all the animal life which would not survive the Flood. The dimensions of the Ark (300 cubits by 50 cubits by 30 cubits) give a cubic capacity of about 1,600,000 cu. ft.

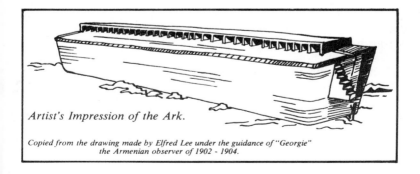

Artist's Impression of the Ark.

Copied from the drawing made by Elfred Lee under the guidance of "Georgie" the Armenian observer of 1902 - 1904.

We can estimate how many animals had to enter the ark by considering the groups that made up the animal life. Ernst Mayr[3] gives the following estimate.

Mammals	3,500 species
Birds	8,600 species
Reptiles and Amphibians . .	5,500 species
Fishes	18,000 species
Tunicates	1,700 species
Echinoderms	4,700 species
Arthropods	815,000 species
Molluscs	88,000 species
Worms	25,000 species
Coelenterates	10,000 species
Sponges	5,000 species
Protozoans	15,000 species
	1,000,000 species

Now many of these groups would have survived in diminished numbers outside the ark and certainly would not have been included. The groups which would definitely be in the ark would be Mammals, birds, Amphibians and Reptiles— a total of only 17,600 species. We are told that two of each were taken on board, and seven of the few clean animals. We can therefore see that the total number of species on board would be no more than 36,000 or thereabouts.

The vast majority of these are, of course, very small but we will make the unlikely assumption that the average size was that of a sheep. So we have 36,000 animals the size of a sheep to accommodate.

Today a railway stock-carrying car has a capacity of 2,670 cubic feet and can carry 240 sheep. The ark was equivalent to about 500 such cars, and was therefore able to carry 500 x 240 sheep = 120,000 sheep.

Yet we don't have 120,000 animals but only one-third of that number, and the vast majority would be smaller than a sheep.

There is sufficient space left over in our calculations to allow for a much greater number of species, and the greater size of animal which could very well have typified the pre-Flood period. Of the larger animals it is likely that Noah took on board the young of the species—undoubtedly mammoths, elephants, dinosaurs, rhinos, hippopotamuses were among the cargo. Inside the Ark many of the animals would have hibernated. To them the journey would have been peaceful and uninterrputed. The shock was yet to come.

Outside the Ark atmospheric conditions were transformed. With the falling rain refraction of the sunlight would have been visible in the sky and the rainbow would have been seen for the first time. It is interesting that it is only after the account of the Flood that Genesis tells of the rainbow (Genesis 9, 12-17).

The instability of the atmosphere was evident—cold winds blew across the land's surface, bringing rain and snow. New mountains higher than ever before now met Noah's eyes and the newly established plant life looked meagre in comparison with the abundance he had last seen. More than that the whole planet was empty of land animals and people—the teeming and well-stocked Earth that had been before, was no more.

After the necessary sacrifices of thanksgiving to God, Noah and his sons went down into the fertile crescent of Mesopotamia and began to till the land and multiply. The animals too left the Ark and began multiplying.

At first the life forms must have appeared much as they were before, but the Earth was now no longer the hot-house it had been and it was not long before growing populations of animals found the climate too harsh for their survival and the food supply too meagre. So it was that the extinction of certain animal groups and species began. Some undoubtedly spread northwards towards the still huge Ice Caps and found themselves unable to adapt sufficiently to the new conditions and perished, unable to survive the rigours of the winter months.

Some spread south along the peninsulas and isthmuses which were present. The Ice Caps were so large that they contained the vast quantities of water which had formerly been in the oceans. The sea level was therefore much lower than it is today, and land bridges existed between islands. At this time Alaska and Northern Siberia were connected; Australia was linked by the Indonesian islands to Asia, and Britain was physically connected to mainland Europe. So many of the species spread and found themselves cut off by the rising waters and the result was highly specialized and protected animal groups which adapted in isolated communities. The Marsupials were one such group. Many, however, found their ideal habitats and settled happily. But the Earth was stabilizing and drying out, and it was soon evident that the ground conditions were changing, gradually driving some animals into more and more restricted habitats and some to the very point of extinction.

Many of these changes of climate are within historical memory. It is thought that as recently as the 13th Century the Aral and Caspian Seas were linked. Continual drying out has now separated them. The present Salt lake in Utah U.S.A. was once a large lake called Lake Bonneville whose past shoreline can still be seen 1,000 feet above the present salt lake level; and the many salt lakes in Nevada are the remains of Lake Lahontan. In many areas the rainfall and rivers removed all the salt, but lakes like lake Titicaca, 12,000 feet up in the Andes, are left as proof of the time when the sea invaded the land.

In the present day Sahara, where there are now only dry wadis and occasional short muddy streams, there are signs of well developed river basins. There were hunters and farmers in the central Sahara whose cave paintings show the abundance of wildlife that used to inhabit that area before the drying out occurred. Lake Victoria in Africa was twice its present size, and so we could go on.

Brontosaurus

From one passage in Job it is clear that some dinosaurs did exist in his day. Job was a man who lived before the Jewish nation came into prominence and who may have been closer to the Flood than to the Exodus. He was an Arab who lived in Uz—today a dry desert area of Arabia. In Job 40: 15-24 is an interesting description of an animal called 'behemoth'. No one knows what the animal was, but the description fits the Brontosaurus very well. 'Look at the behemoth, which I made along with you and which feeds on grass like an ox. What strength he has in his loins, what power in the muscles of his belly! His tail sways like a cedar; the sinews of his thighs are close-knit. His bones are tubes of brass; his limbs like rods of iron. He ranks first among the works of God. Yet his Maker can approach him with his sword. The hills bring him their produce, and the wild animals play nearby. Under the Lotus plant he lies, hidden among the reeds in the marsh. The Lotuses conceal him in their shadow; the poplars by the stream surround him. When the river rages, he is not alarmed; he is secure, though the Jordan should surge against his mouth. Can anyone capture him by the eyes, or trap him and pierce his nose?'

Most people today accept this animal as an elephant or hippopotomus *but* the description doesn't fit. In v.17 we have a verse about his tail—'His tail sways like a cedar'. Here is a strong powerful tail likened to the strongest of trees in the Middle East. Elephants and hippos have minute tails—so small that an elephant's trunk is many times larger than its tail. No—this animal was a mighty land creature—very much a dinosaur among beasts. But even these died out—their carcases rotting or being eaten, and their bones being worn away. So the terrible lizards met extinction leaving nothing but their remains encased in Flood deposits.

It is also in Job that we find Biblical support for the gradual change in climate. In Job 6: 15-17 we read 'My brethren have dealt deceitfully as a brook and as the stream of brooks they pass away; which are blackish by reason of the ice, and wherein the snow is hid: what time they wax warm; they vanish; when it is hot they are consumed out of their place'. Job like all early men used analogies from the world around him—here his analogy is to melting ice and snow. Where in Arabia today would he have seen that?

In Job 37: 6-11 He says to the snow, "Fall on the earth;" and to the rain shower, "Be a mighty downpour." So that all men he has made know his work, he stops every man from his labour. The animals take cover; they remain in their dens. The tempest comes out from its chamber, the cold from the driving winds.

The breath of God produces ice, and the broad waters become frozen. He loads the clouds with moisture; he scatters his lightning through them". Here is a description of whirlwinds, frost, frozen rivers and large clouds. Even more startling! Job 38: 29-30 reads, "From whose womb comes the ice? Who gives birth to the frost from the heavens when the waters become hard as stone, when the surface of the deep is frozen."[4] Here are

Orang-Utang also in danger of extinction

ice covered lakes and even the sea is frozen And remember these are the seas we now call the Persian Gulf, the Indian Ocean, the Red Sea and the Mediterranean!!

The picture we are given is of a climate out of equilibrium, and of an earth which was in a state of adjustment. The microevolutionary adaptations which were soon to become evident were just beginning. Soon large plants established on mountain tops or in exposed northern areas would either die or adapt to the new conditions. Plants which today grow on the Equator and which transpire freely through large leaves often have closely related small-leafed species further north, hiding in cracks from the harsh conditions.

Animals too either moved, adapted or died. The lions and wild animals which inhabited Palestine and the European lions, hyenas and straight-tusked elephants have all become extinct.

References:

1. Professor A.G. Ingalls *'The Carboniferous Mystery'*. Scientific American Vol. 162 p.14 January 1940.

2. C.S. Lewis *'Letters to Malcolm'*.

3. Ernst Mayr — Cited in Theodosius Dobzkansky *'Genetics & the Origin of Species*. (3rd. Ed. New York: Columbia University Press 1951) pp.3-10.

4. Dr. Bernard Northrup *'Light on the Ice Age'*. Bible-Science Newsletter XIV June 1976, 1-4.

CHAPTER SEVEN

Man

As we have seen, the hostile environment after the Flood served to eliminate a number of animal species and to reduce their size and strength. The question that is now important is how the changed conditions affected Man? Before the Flood men were extremely long-living, probably larger in stature than today and because the environment provided an easy living, they may have been technologically advanced. Climate has always influenced Man's culture and the rise and fall of Empires. Many geographers would maintain that the Roman and Greek cultures became so advanced because the friendly climate of the first two centuries B.C. made food production easier and allowed more time to be spent developing culture, the arts and philosophy. This was certainly true in the antediluvian days. We catch a brief glimpse of it in Genesis 4, v.17 where Cain built a city and named it after his son Enoch; and in v.21 where Jubal was 'the father of all who play the harp and flute' i.e. the development of music; and in v.22 where Tubal-cain 'forged all kinds of tools out of bronze and iron' —the development of metal working and craftsmanship. The extent of technology before the Flood cannot be accurately known, but the claims of some to have found remains of electric batteries and advanced metallurgy may not be as far-fetched as most assume.

Once the Flood had become an historical fact and the environment had taken on a hostile stance, the fight for survival would have marked out the early post-Flood years. It has been stated many times that early man was primitive and the assumption is always that man was coming out from monkeyhood and learning the art of Manhood! But that need not be the reason for a more primitive culture. On the Earth today, seemingly primitive cultures are found in areas of extremely inhospitable climates—in desert areas where water supply itself is a daily life or death struggle; or in the icy northern continental fringes where Eskimos eke out an existence. To industrialized nations the remains of abandoned Eskimo villages would look stone-age, but the Eskimos[1] are as intelligent as any race and are part of the modern human scene. They are not primitive, but fully occupied with survival.

So it would be with the post-Flood pioneers. As the families increased they spread out over the Earth's surface. These pioneers, like the American pioneers who went west on wagon-trains, left the more settled conditions in Mesopotamia to travel through India to China and Mongolia, north to Russia, north-west to Europe, south into Africa and south east to Asia and beyond. Man's quest for knowledge and exploration was as strong as ever. Eventually those who settled in Northern China and Eastern Russia i.e. the Mongoloid descendents of Ham, passed over the Bering land bridge into the Americas. In the frozen northern wastes some stayed and became Eskimos, the rest spreading south into the interior of North America. The Red Indians of today are pioneers who stayed there, while others who ventured even further south became the Mayas of Central America and the Incas of South America.

Each tribe carried with it a version of the basic historical story of the Flood, embellished to the point of mythology. Wherever men went the basic tale went too, so that today over 100 human communities have their own remarkably similar versions of the Flood story. Even the men who followed the marsupials down the Indonesian land bridge and became the Australian aborigines have such a story.

As they spread outwards they encountered even more environmentally hostile conditions. The tree life was undeveloped and timber not generally available for either buildings or blazing fires and as result, life was spent in clay houses or in caves. It is Job again who gives us a glimpse into these conditions:- in Job 4: 17, "Can a mortal be more righteous than God? Can a man be more pure than his Maker? If God places no trust in his servants; if he charges his angels with error, how much more those who dwell in houses of clay. whose foundations are in the dust, who are crushed more readily than the moth.'

Here are men dwelling in houses of clay. This is of basic significance to us as far as archaeology is concerned because often cities which are excavated are said to be many thousands of years old because of the many building levels found on the sites. In the ancient world people tended to stay in the same areas and when houses fell down because of earthquake or decay, they levelled the old houses and built new houses on the rubble. This is why many of the ancient sites now appear as mounds or TELS, e.g. TEL ARMARNA or TEL EL FUL (Gibeah) or TEL ED-DUWEIR (Lachish). In many of these TELS, the number of building levels runs into dozens. In the dry conditions of today each level may represent 100-200 years of occupation and if it is assumed that such conditions always prevailed then it is obvious that the history of such sites may date back to 4,000-7,000 B.C.

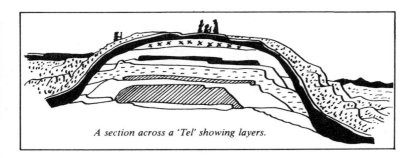

A section across a 'Tel' showing layers.

BUT if the Genesis account of the Flood is correct, conditions would be far from what they are today, indeed in the turbulently humid conditions of the post-Flood era the clay dwellings would have lasted for only a few years at the most. We can therefore see the likelihood that dozens of levels represent only a matter of hundreds not thousands of post-deluvian years, which would mean that these cities are much younger than is generally supposed.[2]

In Job 30: 1-8 we have the cave dwellers—v.6 'to live in the dry stream beds, among the rocks and in holes in the ground.'

Here is a picture of men affected by increased cosmic radiation, a hostile climate, a much poorer diet, a probable vitamin deficiency and damp, often cramped living conditions. The immediate effect would be a dramatic decrease in the expected life-span. The Bible documents this decline in detail and if graphed, the ages can be seen to follow an exponential decay curve.

See graph:-

But there would also have been other effects. Eating habits would have changed. Meat—now permitted in the diet—would have been tough and gristly, needing to be torn from the bones by the teeth, and chewed very strongly. For this an increase in the strength of the muscles of the face would be required, and a strengthening of the parts of the skull on which the muscles are anchored. The skull adapts to such pressures in a very short time by the development of a boney ridge or keel on its top. Such jaw movement pressures affecting the skulls of youngsters would change the whole shape of their skull, and coupled with a likely calcium deficiency would produce a definite low and sloping forehead. Chewing would develop the size of the teeth and as in the skulls of vigorous chewing animals the jaws would be pushed forward. An increased jaw size would produce large pressures acting upwards on the face and as a result brow-ridges would develop to help absorb them. Eventually worn down animal-like teeth would result from

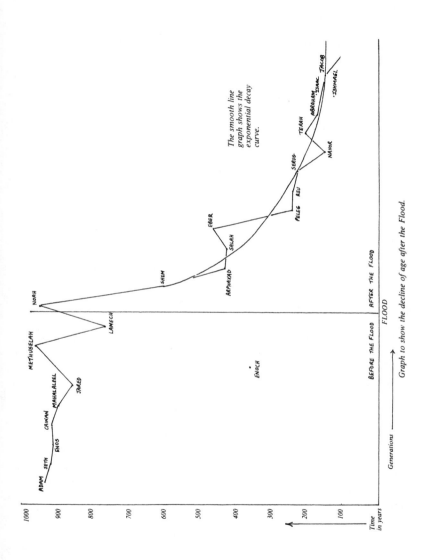

The smooth line graph shows the exponential decay curve.

Graph to show the decline of age after the Flood.

81

vigorous chewing sustained over a long lifespan which, while decreasing, was still greater than our lifespan today.

Such adaptations of the human skull are well researched[3] and both the raw-meat eating Eskimoes and the aboriginal people show this kind of skull development. In less harsh conditions the skull would revert to its former shape.

So these post-Flood pioneers would have skulls which varied in shape according to the pioneering frontiers on which they were found. They are not primitive men, but recent men with their skull shapes adapted to the conditions. The well known Neanderthal man would have been such a man.

It is of great interest to note that the more 'primitive' skull shapes are found well away from the central Mesopotamian region, in Central Europe, Central and Northern China, E. and S. Africa and Indonesia—yet no digs in the Middle East have ever revealed primitive skull types. Undoubtedly this area, first inhabited by Noah after the Flood, possessed a more settled climate, so that this fertile crescent, the 'Cradle of Civilization', represented an area of ease in comparison with those distant from it.

As far as the skeletons of the post-Flood people were concerned it is likely that the meagre diet and damp, cramped conditions would make the people more prone to spinal osteoarthritis, producing in many of them a stooping posture.

It becomes obvious from these considerations that there are two distinct phases in the history of Man—namely antediluvian and postdiluvian. The antediluvian man would appear to all intents and purposes very much like modern man—his skull would be modern in appearance and, because of the ease of living, would have no keel, no protruding jaw, and no boney ridge over the eyes. He would be upright and well-developed. The postdiluvian man on the other hand would show all the signs of degeneration expected in a harsh environment: his skull would have some central keel, an eye-ridge and protruding jaw and he might exhibit some deformity in his skeletal shape.

In the layers of rock laid down in the Flood therefore we would expect to find remains of human skulls and bones which are shaped like those of present day man, lacking the features produced by a hostile environment. In the period in which the Flood occurred both men and the primates would have been mobile and it is likely that they would have died together on the highest and most protected areas. The primates would have been larger than their present day counterparts and would show in their skeletal remains the effects of an hospitable climate. The remains of their skeletons would be intermixed with those of man and the more advanced mammals. Other human finds dating from after the Flood, however, would look more primitive and share some of the characteristics of primates.

These expected finds are in direct contrast with those of an evolutionary model, in which the older human remains would be primitive and the more recent remains progressively more modern in appearance.

The evidence, therefore, is crucial and must be examined.

References:

A. Custance '*Establishing a Palaeolithic IQ'*. Doorway Paper No. 22 P.O. Box 291, Brockville, Ontario, Canada.

2. Charles Clough '*Dawn of the Kingdom'*. A Framework for Basic Christian Doctrine Section III, Lubbock Bible Church, Lubbock, Texas 79410.

3. A. Custance '*The Influence of Environmental Pressures on the Human Skull'*. Doorway Papers No.9 P.O. Box 291, Brockville, Ontario, Canada.

I am indebted to the many works of Arthur C. Custance for basic thoughts behind this chapter.

CHAPTER EIGHT

Is Man a Modern Ape?

Various categories of evidence have been used to demonstrate the Theory of Evolution and the proposed development of man from the apes. Whereas in this chapter we will be more concerned with the fossil record, the significance of physical similarity and vestigial organs must also be considered.

Similarity

The fact that men and monkeys are similar in appearance is the most convincing evidence for evolution as far as most people are concerned, and the assumption underlying their thoughts is that similarity in appearance demonstrates relationship and a common ancestry.

Fortunately such ideas can be tested. Below is a table showing nine plants which all show remarkable similarity, and yet are totally different species growing in different countries and widely different environments.

Plant	Country	Environment
Tree Fern	Java	Mountain Forest
Cycads	Transvaal	Savannah
Palm Trees	Southern California	Semi-arid conditions
Grass Trees	Queensland	Mountains
Puya	Peru	Sub-alpine mountains
Giant Lobelia	East Africa	Mountains
Senecio	Africa	Mountains
Joshua Tree	Southern Nevada	Desert
Cactus	Arizona	Desert

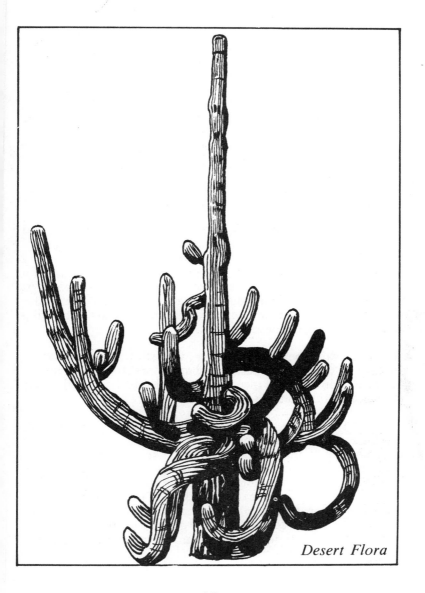

Desert Flora

These plants all have a similar 'umbrella' shape and yet their similarity shows nothing about relationship. Indeed the desert vegetation of Arizona is almost identical in form with the desert vegetation of Africa, yet the former is of the CACTUS family, while the latter is of the SPURGE family.

On the other hand plants known to be related often exhibit a wide dissimilarity. The stinging nettle is a relative of the large forest trees of the mulberry family, and 'Spanish moss'—the grass-like plant often seen festooning telephone wires in Southern U.S.A.—is a close relative of the pineapple.

So it can be seen that form does not depend on taxonomic similarity, nor taxonomic similarity on form.

Nor can one shared characteristic be used as proof of relationship—pigs and sperm whales produce identical insulin while other types of whale differ in this respect from the sperm whale; yet no one would suggest on the basis of insulin similarity that the pig is the closer relative. Rabbits' blood is very similar to that of humans, and rats often have a response to drugs similar to that of Man. Such similarity shows nothing about evolutionary development.

To the Bible-believer however, this shows the hand of a Creator — similarity in design and no more. Men and monkeys look alike in many respects, but that in itself is inadequate evidence of relationship.

The oft repeated dictum that 'Ontogeny recapitulates Phylogeny' is based on similarity. It states that the development of an embryo from the egg to the completed form follows in microcosm the evolutionary development of the animal. The human embryo at one point has folds of tissue which resemble gills, for example, and this used to be taken as a picture of an early stage in our evolutionary development. Needless to say the folds of skin are gill-like in appearance only and have no gill-type structure, and certainly do not supply oxygen to the foetus.

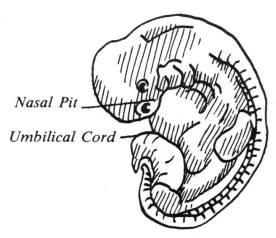

Nasal Pit

Umbilical Cord

Human Embryo at Five Weeks

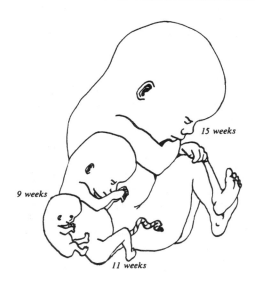

9 weeks

11 weeks

15 weeks

87

Today this idea is not generally accepted as proof of evolutionary development and is not normally used by academics. It is interesting to note that a monkey embryo looks more human than the new born monkey, and if the form of the embryo did demonstrate the path of evolution it would suggest that monkeys evolved from men and that apes should be at the summit of evolutionary development.

Carved statues may all look similar in the early stages of work, but this in no way implies that any one has been based on another. So in the formation of embryos, masses of protoplasm are being moulded and may assume similar shapes at first, but this is not evidence of evolution.

Vestigial Organs
At one time it was thought that because the human body had evolved it would contain certain organs which had a use in former times but which eventually came to serve no purpose. It was assumed that these remnants from the past would gradually shrink until they were no longer found in the human body.

This was very much in line with evolutionary thinking and when first listed, 180 such vestigial organs were included. As medical knowledge has extended, however, the number of organs designated as vestigial has decreased dramatically and is now practically zero. Examples of organs once considered vestigial are:- the appendix, the thymus, the thyroid, the tonsils and the coccyx. Doctors now know that the appendix helps in the prevention of illness; the thymus produces essential antibodies; the thyroid produces hormones; the tonsils help fight local infections; and the coccyx is a vital anchor point for muscles. Far from being 'left over' organs from an earlier stage of development they all have important functions.

Fossil Evidence
We now consider what is the main-stay of the ape-man evolutionary theory.

The story of the evidence of Fossil Man is one of the most complex and difficult studies to undertake. The reason for this is that many have come and 'muddied the water' and detailed descriptions based on mere fragments of bone have been made. The major problem is expressed well by Prof. Wilson D. Wallis. He pointed out that 'there is a kind of law in the matter of anthropological thinking about fossil remains which goes something like this: the less information we have by reason of the scarcity and antiquity of the remains, the more sweeping can our generalizations be about them. If you find the bones of a man who has died recently you have to be rather careful what you say about him because someone might be able to check up on your conclusions. The further you go back, the more confidently you can discuss such reconstructions because there is less possibility of anyone being able to challenge you'.[1]

The point is that bold statements have often been made on insufficient grounds, or worse still that real evidence has been explained away or even ignored. It is also true to say that occasionally some deception has been practised. But has man developed from apes or not? The evolutionist must say 'yes', the creationist 'no'. What is the evidence?

To clarify the situation it is necessary to review the history of fossil man. Palaeoanthropologists today trace the recognizable line of man from ape in five overlapping stages. These stages are given as:-
1. Ramapithecus
2. Australopithecus
3. Homo Erectus
4. Varieties of Homo Sapiens
5. Modern forms of Homo Sapiens

Let us take this *proposed* line and analyse it.

1.   **Ramapithecus.** Many evolutionists assume Ramapithecus to have been the first recognizable man-like ape, who they say came onto the scene 14 million years ago.

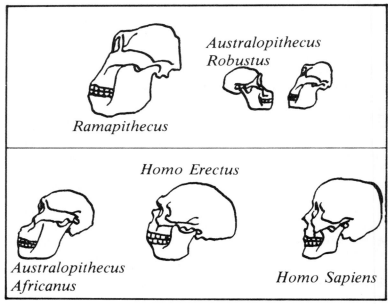

Fossil Skulls

It is vital to note that the descriptions of Ramapithecus are conjectural only. Weiner's book 'Man's Natural History'[2] shows this well . . . 'because we *believe* that Ramapithecus lived in open country . . . we may *assume* that . . .' '*If* the Ramapithecines *were* . . .' 'As Ramapithecus *may have done* . . .' 'Like the chimpanzees the Ramapithecines *may* have used simple tools.' All is 'may have' 'If . . . then' 'we assume' and so on. (Author's emphases.)

What is the fossil evidence behind Ramapithecus?

The first fossil of Ramapithecus was found in the Siwalik hills of India in 1932-4. It consisted of part of a right upper jaw having two premolar and two molar teeth as well as sockets for canine and incisor teeth. Later more of these jaw bones and teeth were found both in India and in Kenya (Kenyapithecus).

The main points noted were that:
1. The front teeth were like present day man's teeth, small in comparison with the back teeth.
2. That the jaw was not U-shaped as in most apes, but more parabolic like the jaw of man.

On the basis of these fragments of jaw and a few teeth it was decided that here was a forefather of Man. But while Simons, Pilbearn and others accept the fossils as those of a human forerunner, others do not and Ramapithecus has been the subject of tremendous controversy.

While it is true that most monkeys do not share these mandibular similarities with man, a recent study of a species of baboon in Ethiopia showed that here at any rate was one living monkey species which does—and it is 100% ape. Even without this research most anthropologists had been convinced that Ramapithecus was an ape anyway. After extensive and detailed studies Dr. Robert Eckhard of The Pennsylvania State University expressed their view by saying that the Ramapithecines 'nevertheless seem to have been apes—morphologically, ecologically and behaviourally'.[3] And so say all of us!

2. **Australopithecus.** We now move firmly into Africa and, according to evolutionists, on in time by 12 million years to 2 million years B.P. (before present). The South African professor of anatomy Raymond A. Dart was the first to identify Australopithecus in 1924 from pieces of a skull found in a quarry not far from Johannesburg. It was said to be part of the cranium of a five or six year old child and so nicknamed 'Dart's baby'. This discovery was largely ignored until the publication of work by Robert Broom who excavated in other parts of South Africa and the famous Dr. L. S. B. Leakey who worked in the Olduvai Gorge, East Africa.

Since 1924 a large number of fossil remains classed under the heading of Australopithecus have been found. The remains are said to be 'man from the waist down—ape from the waist up'.

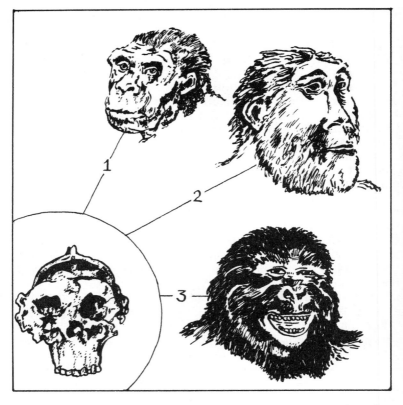

Original Fossil Skull which formed the basis of the 3 reconstructions of
Zinjanthropus.

1. Zinjanthropus, drawn for the Sunday Times of 5th April 1964.

2. Zinjanthropus, drawn by Neave Parker for Dr. L.S.B. Leakey, and published by the illustrated London News and Sketch, 1st January 1960.

3. Zinjanthropus, drawn by Maurice Wilson for Dr. Kenneth P. Oakley.

The major features of the skeletons were:-
1. The skull capacity was 450-650 c.c. (c.f. 1450 c.c. in man; and 400-500 c.c. in Ramapithecus).
2. A pelvis showing a slightly stooping posture with the head definitely downward.
3. Small stature—only 4′ tall.
4. A jaw similar to that of Ramapithecus—i.e. small front teeth and a parabolic jaw shape. Furthermore because the back teeth were huge the jaws were much larger than those of present day chimpanzees.

The main types found have been named:-
(a) Australopithecus africanus—probably carnivorous
(b) Australopithecus robustus—probably herbivorous
(c) Dr. L. Leakey's famous Zinjanthropus bosei or East-African Man.

In Science News[4] it was revealed that Dr. Louis Leakey's son and successor, Richard Leakey has collected fossil limb bones of Australopithecus and found them to have very long arms but very short legs! This would mean that Austrolopithecus walked like many modern apes i.e. 'a long-armed, short-legged Knuckle-Walker'.

The posture then is that of an ape, the brain size is that of an ape, the jaw structure is that of an ape—it looks very much as if we have here some more apes.

Two other groups also have to be considered—the so called HOMO HABILIS and SKULL 1470.

Homo Habilis
These remains were found in 1960 by Louis Leakey in the Olduvai Gorge in Tanzania. He dated the finds as 1.8 million years old. What marked Homo Habilis out to Leakey was that he said it had a larger and more modern shape of skull, and there was evidence of the use of tools.

Leakey himself does not believe Homo Habilis to be a more

modern version of Australopithecus but a different evolutionary line altogether[5]. Others feel that Homo Habilis was simply a type of Australopithecus Africanus.

The problem with this is that the cranial capacity is still more apish than human,(680 c.c.—estimate by Tobias)[6] and that while the creature may have *used* tools there is no evidence that it ever *made* them. The difference is crucial—birds often use tools e.g. stones to crack open snail shells. That is an altogether different matter from making them. Even present day monkeys grab stones and hit things with them.

Manufactured tools have been found but it is not accepted that AUSTRALOPITHECUS or HOMO HABILIS made them,but rather that early 'true man' hunted Australopithecus and then left the tools.[7]

Homo Habilis then is still probably an ape.

Skull 1470
In 1972 Richard E. Leakey found a skull he dated as 2.8 million years old i.e. much older than those of the Australopithicines and Homo Habilis. It was found East of Lake Rudolph and was fairly complete. Since then a further skull belonging to a five or six year old has been found as well as other skeletal bones.

'Astonishingly' the skull is extremely modern in appearance. It was much larger in capacity, had no brow ridges, a high, not sloping, forehead and no 'keel'. Altogether modern—yet older than the more primitive shaped skulls. Such a skull would be totally out of line with evolutionary expectations and Richard Leakey himself has admitted that this skull means that he must start again in his thinking. But as we have seen, the find of such a skull in lower strata would fit in perfectly with what we would expect to find after a Universal Flood.

3. **Homo Erectus** (800,000-300,000 B.P.)
Evolutionists declare Homo erectus (or Pithecanthropus

erectus as he is sometimes called) to be the next stage, and the first real member of the genus Homo , estimated as having lived about 750,000 B.C. The major difference is the larger brain size (1100 c.c.) and the upright walking position.

There are four main members of the group—
A. Java Man B. Peking Man C. Heidelberg Man; and D. Meganthropus. But all of these have associated problems.

A. **Java Man**
Java Man was the first claimant to the title of Homo Erectus. The bones were discovered by a Dutchman called Eugene Dubois on a terrace cut by the River Solo in Java in 1891. He found the top of a skull which he said showed a cranial capacity of 900 c.c. (though that was a guess because it is impossible to work out the cranial capacity from such a fragment)—he also later found a thigh bone and three teeth which he assumed came from the same type of man. The thigh bone was exactly the same as those found in modern man.

But it was at this point that the truth about the finds placed grave doubts on the validity of Dubois' work. For although he didn't say anything to anyone for thirty years after, Dubois had found two obviously modern human skulls in the same area as Java man *and at a lower level* making them, by uniformitarianism, older. But Dubois didn't mention these until he had convinced the world that Pithecanthropus was man-like. What is more, before he died Dubois himself said that he viewed the skull-cap as that of a large gibbon and no more. His conclusions were also those of many who carried out a detailed study of the remains. Even Encyclopaedia Britannica[8] says 'The skull cap is astonishingly small and presents a remarkable simian (monkey-like) appearance'.

And yet these facts are not recounted and in modern evolutionary books Java man is stated as a factual forefather of modern man. The thigh bone was that of a true man. Two of the teeth were those of an orang-utang and one of a modern man! Here was a site where man and monkey had coexisted, not one which demonstrated ancestry and lineage.

B. Peking Man

Here is an even more complex story. Again, the Encyclopaedias and text books treat Peking Man or Homo Erectus Pekinensis as undisputed fact, but actually the case is far from proven. The first discoveries were made by Prof. Davidson Black in 1927—he is said to have found one lower molar tooth and then in 1929 a well-preserved skull in the same area of Chou-k'ou-tien near Peking. When Prof. Black died the work was handed on to Prof. Franz von Weidenreich. By the time World War I occurred many skulls, jaw bones and teeth had apparently been found and models based on them had been made.

But here is the twist of the story. During the Japanese invasion of China all the material vanished except for two of the teeth, and not one person was able to give a satisfactory explanation of what happened to the finds.

Hence we have no evidence for Peking man except two teeth, the eye-witness accounts given by certain evolutionists, and some models which they had made.

At this time people were very keen to find the remains of early man and very often the analysis of results was biased. Two very famous 'mistakes' made at this time were the Hesperopithecus or Nebraska Man, and the now famous Piltdown Man. After five years' research on the one tooth(!) found as the evidence of Nebraska Man it was proved to be from a wild pig. It is interesting that drawings or artist's impressions had been made of Nebraska Man and they all looked vaguely human, not like a pig at all.

Piltdown Man was based on a jaw bone and part of a skull found in 1912 and was only uncovered as a hoax in 1953. From 1912-1950 it was declared to be 500,000 years old and a missing link. Only with the modern tests devised after the War was it found to be recent but treated with chemicals to take on an old appearance.

Like Nebraska Man, Peking Man came into being after the find of one tooth yet Peking Man is now untouchable, being no longer available for modern analysis. All we now have are models made by Black and Weidenreich who certainly would have made them appear to be what they thought they were—representatives of a group intermediate between a gorilla and a man.

As for Heidelberg Man (C) and Meganthropus (D) the facts are inconclusive. Heidelberg man was named after a massive jaw found in 1907 in a sand-pit at Mauer in Germany. This is the only find associated with Heidelberg Man and while the jaw itself is considered by all to be typically monkey-like, the teeth are considered human. The earlier discussions about Ramapithecus show the problems concerned with the shape of teeth.

Meganthropus again is identified by lower jaw fragments and teeth and these are seen by many to be the same as those of Australopithecus.

So the evidence for Homo erectus is fragmentary, uncertain and in some cases very disturbing.

4. **Varieties of Homo Sapiens** (dated by evolutionists at 75,000 B.C.)
Here the remains are definitely those of human beings and include Neanderthal, Cromagnon and Swanscombe man. These were the post-flood pioneers. Indeed not only did Neanderthal Man walk upright but his cranial capacity actually exceeded that of modern man. If our conclusions about the conditions existing before the Flood are correct then this would be no surprise and the deterioration of conditions, while affecting the shape of the skull, and the posture, would only gradually cause a reduction in overall skull size.

The remains of these men show all the signs of the vitamin deficiency, arthritis and rickets[9] outlined in the previous chapter, while the associated artifacts show the existence of a definite human culture. Cave drawings abound, showing the hand to mouth existence of the pioneers.

Here then is the fossil evidence. It shows clearly that there is no tree of development, but rather a haphazard conglomeration of finds. Skull 1470 is that of a modern man found deep in the Earth, a find to be expected if a universal flood had occurred. Ape skulls are found intermixed with human bones in areas where both co-existed.

A summary of the finds shows that amazing statements and ideas have been based on very little evidence.

Ramapithecus	Based on jaw bones and a few teeth	Ape
Australopithecines	Skulls and other skeletal bones	Ape
Peking Man	Fragments of skull, jawbones and teeth. Evidence lost.	
Java Man	Skull cap, 3 teeth and thigh bone	Ape
Heidelberg Man	A jaw	?
Meganthropus	Fragments of jawbones and teeth	Ape
Piltdown Man	A hoax	
Neanderthal man	Skulls and other parts of the skeleton	A man
Homo Habilis	Part of a skull	Probably an ape
Skull 1470	Several skulls	A man

So no support can be given by the fossil evidence to the Evolutionist's hypothesis, but this evidence does fit the expectations of the Creationist; that of a special Creation followed by a catastrophe of Universal proportions.

What causes the rejection of such a scheme is that it demands the existence of a God of Righteousness and Justice who personally intervenes in the arena of the Earth's history. It is the only alternative to an Evolutionary Framework, and as such is unacceptable to the sinful, autonomous human heart. God's promise is that there will never be another Universal Flood 'And I will remember my covenant which is between me and you and every living creature of all flesh; and the waters shall no more become a flood to destroy all flesh'. Genesis 9: 15.

But the Bible doesn't end at that point for in 2 Peter 3: 7 and 9 it warns of what is to come. 'But the heavens and the earth which are now, by the same word are kept in store, reserved unto fire against the day of judgment and ungodly men'. 'The Lord is not slack concerning his promise as some count slackness, but is long suffering to usward, *not willing that any should perish but that all should come to repentance.*'

The glory and wonder is that knowing the Judgment ahead, God has provided the way of escape, sending Jesus to suffer on the Cross for our sins that He might satisfy the Righteousness and Justice of God, and extend to all who will believe on Him the love and forgiveness of God. For 'those who call upon the Name of the Lord shall be saved'.

References:

1. Prof. Wilson D. Wallis in *'Pro-Suppositions in Anthropological Interpretations'*. American Anthropologist. July - Sept. 50: 1948 p. 560. Quoted from A. Custance. Doorway Paper No. 'Fossil Man and Genesis'.

2. J. W. Weiner *'Man's Natural History'*. P.

3. Dr. Robert Eckhard.

4. Science News Vol. 100 p. 387 (27th November 1971).

5. W. L. Straus Jnr. *'Australopithecines Contemporaneous with Man?'* Science 1926; 1957 p. 1238.

6. P. W. Tobias *'The Olduvai Bed I Hominine with Special Reference to its Cranial Capacity'*. Nature (1964) 202 (4927):3.

7. L. S. B. Leakey *'Homo Habilis, Homo Erectus and Australopithecines'* Nature 209: 1966 p. 1280 and 1281.

8. Encyclopaedia Britannica Vol. 14 p. 739. 1973.

9. *'Neanderthals had Rickets'* Science Digest Vol. 69 p. 35 Feb. 1971.

Books and Tapes by Roger Price

Books

Victory in Jesus   (reprinted Aug 1991)   £2.95
     A manual for victorious Christian living

Possessing the Land   (1984)   £1.95
     The balance between faith and works

God's Wonderful Family   (1986)   £2.25
     Growing up as mature sons in His family

These are available from Christian bookshops or post free from the address below.

Bible Study Tapes (and Videos)

Roger recorded around 275 studies during his life, including nearly 100 Basic Bible Studies — a foundational course for all Christians. A few are also available on video.

Full Catalogues of tapes, books and videos may be obtained from:

> CCF Tapes
> 30 Crescent Road
> BOGNOR REGIS   W Sussex
> England   PO21 1QG

*Further copies of **In the Beginning** may also be obtained, £3.95 post free, from this address, or through your Christian bookshop.*